The Mole

CONTENTS

UNIT S1 - THE MOLE

30689131

PREFACE

This volume is one of twenty Units produced by ILPAC, the Independent Learning Project for Advanced Chemistry, written for students preparing for the Advanced Level examinations of the G.C.E. The Project has been sponsored by the Inner London Education Authority and the materials have been extensively tested in London schools and colleges. In its present revised form, however, it is intended for a wider audience; the syllabuses of all the major Examination Boards have been taken into account and questions set by these boards have been included.

Although ILPAC was initially conceived as a way of overcoming some of the difficulties presented by uneconomically small sixth forms, it has frequently been adopted because its approach to learning has certain advantages over more traditional teaching methods. Students assume a greater responsibility for their own learning and can work, to some extent, at their own pace, while teachers can devote more time to guiding individual students and to managing resources.

By providing personal guidance, and detailed solutions to the many exercises, supported by the optional use of video-cassettes, the Project allows students to study A-level chemistry with less teacher-contact time than a conventional course demands. The extent to which this is possible must be determined locally; potentially hazardous practical work must, of course, be supervised. Nevertheless, flexibility in time-tabling makes ILPAC an attractive proposition in situations where classes are small or suitably-qualified teachers are scarce.

In addition, ILPAC can provide at least a partial solution to other problems. Students with only limited access to laboratories, for example, those studying at evening classes, can concentrate upon ILPAC practical work in the laboratory, in the confidence that related theory can be systematically studied elsewhere. Teachers of A-level chemistry who are inexperienced, or whose main discipline is another science, will find ILPAC very supportive. The materials can be used effectively where upper and lower sixth form classes are timetabled together. ILPAC can provide 'remedial' material for students in higher education. Schools operating sixth form consortia can benefit from the cohesion that ILPAC can provide in a fragmented situation. The project can be adapted for use in parts of the world where there is a severe shortage of qualified chemistry teachers. And so on.

A more detailed introduction to ILPAC, with specific advice both to students and to teachers, is included in the first volume only. Details of the Project Team and Trial Schools appear inside the back cover.

LONDON 1983

ACKNOWLEDGEMENTS

Thanks are due to the following examination boards for permission to reproduce questions from past A-level papers:

University of London Entrance and School Examinations Council:

    Exercises 24(N 1977), 35(L 1980)

    Level One Test 7 (L 1978)

Questions from other examination boards appear in other Units.

Where answers to these questions are included, they are provided by ILPAC and not by the examination board.

Photographs of students by Tony Langham.

First published 1983
by John Murray (Publishers) Ltd
50 Albemarle Street
London W1X 4BD

Reprinted 1984

Printed and bound in Great Britain by
Martin's of Berwick

British Library Cataloguing in Publication Data

Independent Learning Project for Advanced
  Chemistry
  The Mole. - (ILPAC; Unit S1)
  1. Science
  I. Title II. Series
  500   Q161.2

  ISBN 0 7195 4035 6

INTRODUCTION TO ILPAC - FOR THE STUDENT

You are about to spend up to two years studying A-level chemistry - so please spend a few minutes reading these notes before you begin. This is important and could save you time and effort later.

Firstly, we shall consider ways of studying effectively; secondly, we shall see how ILPAC can help.

HOW SHOULD I STUDY?

You may never have asked yourself this question. Your teacher may have guided you so carefully that you have simply had to follow instructions - to copy notes from the blackboard, perhaps, and then to learn them and copy them out again for a test! This can be quite a good way of learning facts, but it doesn't really help you to solve problems. It protects you from thinking and taking decisions - the teacher has done that for you.

As you move towards more advanced studies, however, you must take more responsibility for your own learning - the ability to find things out for yourself is really one of the most valuable skills you can develop and, despite the electronic revolution, your most useful aids are still books.

How to use a textbook

Books differ in style and content and you are unlikely to find all you need for A-level chemistry in a single volume. Don't be put off if you still don't understand the topic you looked up after reading about it in one book - try another one. If you are still in difficulties, then you should go to your teacher, but you'll be surprised how quickly you realise the strengths and weaknesses of the books available to you.

"How should I read a book? Surely that's obvious - start at the beginning and keep going!" Yes, of course, if you are reading a novel. But a textbook is different. It is a mine of information, but it tells you more than you need to know to solve a particular problem. The art of using a textbook is to be selective. Look through the book to see how it breaks the subject down into chapters, sections and sub-sections. Make good use of the index, and do not be afraid to start reading in the middle of a chapter. To use an index sensibly, of course, you will need to look up significant words - 'keywords' - and, as we shall see, ILPAC can help you to do this.

So, let us suppose that you have found the right section of the textbook. What next? Well, read it and make a few notes. But is that advice as simple as it sounds? There are different ways of reading, and there are different ways of making notes. Let's look at this more closely:

Styles of reading

It is useful (although a little artificial) to divide methods of reading into three styles: scanning, skimming and intensive reading.

Scanning simply means running the eye rapidly down a page to search for particular words or phrases. To see how quickly you can scan a page, look up a word in the index of your textbook, say 'electron'. Turn to the first reference and look down the page so rapidly that the words are just a blur. Then slow down and look at the page again. Keep doing this, more slowly each time, until you can pick out the word you are looking for.

Skimming is slower than scanning and involves reading a passage to get an idea of its contents. Having skimmed through it, you should know whether or not the passage would repay closer study. If you cannot find what you want in one book by skimming, try another book.

Intensive reading means reading every word and studying the passage, sentence by sentence, until you have gained all the relevant information it contains.

Do remember that reading, at whatever depth, must be an active process. Be clear about what it is that you are looking for (ILPAC objectives are useful here - see below) and read for a purpose. It is quite possible to sit with glazed eyes at an open book and learn nothing!

Styles of note-taking

Your notes are for your benefit and, so long as they are accurate and under-standable by you, then they will serve their purpose. Two general points are worth making.

(1) The better you have understood the material, the briefer will be your notes. They will then act as 'triggers' for your memory.

(2) You should never copy out sections of text (except, perhaps, definitions and laws). Copied-out notes, neatly underlined, look reassuring but may simply be undigested material that you have not really thought about.

There are at least two distinct styles of notemaking and these can be labelled 'linear' and 'patterned'.

Linear notes are ordered sequences of information, with headings and sub-headings.

Patterned notes are made by grouping words or phrases round a central idea.

To illustrate the differences between these two styles, here are some notes made on what has been written so far in this introduction.

ILPAC Intro – Hints on Study generally + ILPAC specifically

A. How to Study.

1. Copied notes not much good. Discourages thinking + Independence

2. Textbooks.
a) Look at Overall Structure
b) Use index – Keywords.
c) Scan – quick look to locate keywords.
d) Skim – identify useful passages.
e) Intensive reading – thorough job.
f) Active reading. Read for a purpose.

3. Notes
a) Brief 'Triggers'
b) Don't copy chunks of text (except def's, Laws?)
c) Linear notes – like these!
d) Patterned notes – web of linked ideas radiating from central theme.

4. . . . .
. . . . , , ,

Whether you think these examples are particularly good notes does not really matter - that would be the concern of the students who wrote them. But do stop and ask yourself how you would have tackled the same job. Bear in mind that linear notes tend to be rather cut-and-dried (which may be appropriate) and that patterned notes are open-ended. You can always add to them and they encourage you to find connections between ideas that might not otherwise have occurred to you. In the end, however, you must develop whatever style suits you best - perhaps a combination of linear and patterned, depending upon the subject matter.

A reading strategy: SQR^3

Let us return to our first question - "How should I study?" Research on how people learn shows that effective reading can be divided into stages. Here are five things you should do:-

1. Survey the material you are going to read to get an overall view (e.g. scan the index and skim the more promising references).

2. Question yourself: "Why am I doing this reading? What am I trying to find out?"

3. Read intensively the passages that you have chosen.

4. Recall: try to remember the main points from the passage you have just read. This may be an effort, but it is an important step in learning. Now is the time to make notes.

5. Review: check your notes against the passage to make sure that nothing important has been missed, and then look through your notes from time to time during the next day or two. Students who take two or three minutes to review notes within 24 hours of making them retain more of what they learn.

This reading strategy has been called, for short, SQR^3 (and sometimes SQ3R).

Time allocation for study

When to study. You will benefit more from doing an hour or two each night than by trying to catch up at weekends or in holidays. Too much study in a single day only results in inefficient learning. Try to establish your own routine, setting aside a couple of hours each night, or at least on the nights when you've had chemistry that day. Don't forget your other subjects either!

Making study sessions effective. Researchers have shown that we concentrate best for periods of 20 - 40 minutes without a break. After this time our attention wanders and studying efficiency falls off rapidly. So, give your-self a break every half hour or so - it may just be enough to get up and walk across the room or to have a chat with someone or look out of the window.

Try to spend between one and three hours on a study session. If you find it difficult to get started, set yourself an easy task first, such as a short exercise. Getting this right will encourage you to carry on with the next task.

Resource-based learning

Books are essential, but are not the only sources of information. You can find out about chemistry in many ways - by watching films and television, by using computer programmes, by making models, by visiting factories and laboratories and, of course, by doing experiments. These sources of information can be called resources. There is a further resource which must be added, perhaps the most important of all, the teacher. The contrast between resource-based learning and more traditional methods is conveniently illustrated by imagining two teachers at work.

The first, Mr. A, is a traditionalist. He stands at the front of the class, explains the subject, gives full notes, asks questions and, once a week, supervises a practical lesson. Homework is set and marked but Mr. A has such a lot of information to convey that he does not have much time to deal with individual difficulties. Because virtually all information comes through the teacher, the class moves forward together at the same steady pace. (A few of the pupils find the pace too rapid and are having difficulties, but they prefer to sit quietly - it's embarrassing to hold up the rest by constantly asking questions. Others find the pace slow and are somewhat bored.) Mr. A's examination results are good, and all agree that he is an effective teacher.

Ms. B is equally respected, and her results are also good but her approach is quite different. She is fond of saying "Why should I tell you when you can find out for yourself?" At first, her pupils are a little disconcerted - but they soon realise that Ms. B has not abandoned them. She has prepared what she calls 'Study Guides' - notes on each topic, with advice on what to read, what experiments to do, what difficulties to look out for, and so on. And, because she does not spend a great deal of time in lecturing the class, she can afford to deal with individual problems and to take part in discussions. Ms. B's pupils can work more or less at their own pace, but she keeps a close watch on each person's progress, and no one is allowed to fall seriously behind. Ms. B, who believes in resource-based learning, regards herself as a sort of manager; it is her job to make sure that the right resources (including her knowledge and skills) are available to the pupils at the right time.

USING ILPAC

ILPAC is designed to assist resource-based learning, sometimes called 'individualised learning'. The course is based on twenty Units, which are not textbooks but guides to study. The first four form an essential starting block, after which various routes are possible. As you encounter various activities for the first time while working through the first three Units, you will find advice on how to proceed.

Here we include short notes on the main features of ILPAC to give you an overview of the structure of a Unit.

1. Levels

Each Unit is divided into two Levels. In most cases, Level One provides an introduction to the topic; Level Two takes you up to Advanced Level. In some Units, the Levels simply divide the work into two subject areas. At the end of a Unit you may find appendices and suggestions for further work.

2. Objectives

Objectives are statements, listed at the beginning of each section, which say what you should be able to do once you have finished that section. They are also a guide to important points to look for in your reading and contain key words to help you use the index of a textbook. You should also find them useful as a framework for making notes. There may be words and phrases in the objectives which are unfamiliar to you. Don't worry about this; at the end of the section you should understand them.

3. Reading

You will not find all the information you need in an ILPAC Unit - we encourage you to study many topics by reading about them in textbooks and often give some guidance on points to look for and pitfalls to avoid. You should use the preceding objectives, especially the keywords, to help you find suitable passages to give purpose to your reading, and to help you make notes.

Your understanding of what you have read is usually tested by one or more exercises; looking at these will also guide your reading.

4. Tests

Each Unit includes three Tests: one at the beginning to check on what you should know beforehand, and one at the end of each Level. Questions from past A-level examination papers are used wherever possible. These tests should normally be marked by your teacher to help monitor your progress.

5. Exercises

There are numerous exercises throughout the course, including A-level questions, to help you check your progress and to give you practice in what you have just learned. One of the main features of ILPAC is the provision of detailed answers to all these exercises at the back of each Unit; another is the inclusion of worked examples to show you how to tackle many different types of numerical problems.

Also included are some revealing exercises, which lead you step by step, in a series of short questions and answers, through some more difficult or lengthy concepts.

A few exercises are intended to be marked by your teacher. These give you practice in essay-type questions, and help your teacher to monitor your progress.

6. Video programmes

A series of video-cassettes has been made to accompany the Units. When using a video-recorder, remember that it can be stopped and restarted whenever you want, and that it is easy to repeat sections of the material. If the video-cassettes are not available, don't worry. Although they are very helpful, you can still follow ILPAC without them.

7. Experiments

Experiments are integrated with the course and have a variety of functions in the ILPAC scheme: some are designed to help you develop essential practical skills, others to illustrate theoretical points. There are also opportunities for you to plan your own experimental work.

Ideally, you should do the experiment at the time you reach it in the text, but you may have to plan ahead in order to make best use of limited laboratory time. Most A-level examinations include a practical test or a practical assessment by the teacher, and a written record of your work will help you to achieve a suitable standard. We give detailed suggestions for writing up practical work in the first Unit.

We include hazard symbols where appropriate - look out for them and take proper precautions.

8. Computer programmes

There are a number of computer programmes available which are particularly relevant to some of the more mathematical topics in the course. They introduce some variety to your activities and may help you to understand some ideas better. However, as with the video programmes, you can still follow the ILPAC course without them.

Planning ahead

Finally, a note about planning your time on the ILPAC course.

One of the advantages of resource-based learning is that it gives you more control over your own time. The Units allow you to see the whole span of work in a topic and to plan ahead. Within reason, you can work through the material at your own pace.

How long you spend on ILPAC each week depends largely on your own organisation and speed of working. As a guide, we recommend between 12 and 15 hours of work each week, but this _is_ only a guide. You should get an idea of how long you need to spend each week by seeing how long you take to complete each of the first few Units and comparing this with the times we recommend. Don't worry if you seem a bit slow on these early Units - it takes time to adjust to the new way of working needed for resource-based learning.

Taking 15 hours per week as an average, we assume that you'll be time-tabled for 4 or 5 hours which leaves between 7 and 11 hours for you to work on your own. Of course, everyone will not reach the same standard, or cover the same material by studying for the same time. You must decide, in due course, what is realistic for you.

We hope you enjoy using the ILPAC scheme and wish you all the best in your study of A-level chemistry.

INTRODUCTION TO ILPAC - FOR THE TEACHER

We expect that you have already read the students' introductory notes (just as we expect the students will read this section!) and will know something about resource-based learning as it is employed in ILPAC Units. The students have been told that you are their most valuable resource - how can you best fulfil this role and how will it differ from conventional teaching?

We believe that using ILPAC is intrinsically worthwhile because it releases students and teachers from some of the constraints of traditional chemistry teaching: we hope that you will agree, even if you have adopted ILPAC primarily to solve logistical problems concerned with staffing, falling rolls and time-tabling. The students are freed from total dependence on the teacher as the sole source of information and guidance and are encouraged to assume a greater measure of responsibility for their own learning. The teacher is freed from the obligation to tell the student everything; there is no need to write out a text-book on the blackboard on a two-yearly cycle!

However, resource-based learning is just as demanding of the teacher as any other approach. Time which might otherwise have been devoted to the dictation of notes is used instead to help pupils on an individual basis, to organise the laboratory and the resources and to monitor progress. This organising and monitoring function is vital; you will be just as important to your students as before but your role will change to that of manager and consultant.

We hope you will find it useful to read the more detailed pieces of advice which now follow.

1.   Plan the whole course with an approximate time-table. If you are using all the ILPAC Units, remember that the first four form an essential 'starting-block'. Thereafter, various routes are possible - some examples are given at the end of this section. If you are using isolated Units, look at these routes to see how they can best fit in with your other work.

2.   Assuming 50 weeks in a two-year course, the <u>average</u> time for the completion of a Unit is 2½ weeks, but some take much longer, especially when resource-based learning is new. Aim to cover about half the course in the first year, even though this is more than half the time available - students always work faster in the second year.

3.   Make sure you are familiar with each Unit before giving it to your students. Ideally, you should work through the whole Unit yourself, including answering the exercises. You may find that some sections can be omitted for your examination syllabus, and you can save a lot of time for your students by foreseeing difficulties. You may also be able to suggest short-cuts for weaker students.

4.   Set a deadline for the completion of each Unit. Although this seems to contradict the spirit of individualised learning, examination dates make it essential. It is better for a weaker student to cover three-quarters of each Unit (with advice on what to miss - see 3 above) than to cover only three-quarters of the course.

5. Monitor progress towards the deadline. A good way of doing this is to pin up a copy of the Contents list for each Unit and make students initial it when they have completed each main section.

6. Look at the way your students make notes and tackle the exercises - they may need more help than they will ask for. Class discussions on these matters (and others) may be helpful. If you and/or your students are new to resource-based learning, expect a 'running-in' period at the beginning of the course when progress is slow. If you persevere, the rate of progress will increase dramatically.

7. Read the Teachers' and Technicians' Notes. Make sure that the apparatus for experiments is suitable, and available when required. Ideally, each student should be able to do each experiment as he or she reaches it in the Unit. This may mean having the same apparatus available for several lessons, or several different experiments going on at the same time.

8. Encourage students to plan ahead so that they make best use of laboratory time, especially if this is limited.

9. Each student should be issued with at least one suitable text-book and a data book and should have access to a variety of others both in the laboratory and the school library. When there are not enough books to go round, ensure that borrowing is organised fairly.

10. Build up a collection of references so that the available books are used to best advantage. Encourage students to contribute to this as they discover which books provide the best coverage of particular topics.

11. If possible, make arrangements to show ILPAC video-cassettes at appropriate times. To make the best use of these video programmes, students should be able to see them more than once and stop/restart the tapes themselves in the laboratory. However, the videotapes are not essential to the course.

12. Remember that your students' attitude towards ILPAC will depend very much on your own - enthusiasm is infectious! If your situation seems to be less than ideal, remember that ILPAC has been tested successfully in many schools and colleges and, in some of these, conditions were far from perfect.

Good luck!

TITLES OF ILPAC UNITS

Starter Units

S1 The Mole

S2 Atomic Structure

S3 Chemical Energetics

S4 Bonding and Structure

Inorganic Chemistry

I1 *s*-Block Elements

I2 The Halogens

I3 The Periodic Table

I4 Group IV Elements

I5 Transition Elements

I6 Selected *p*-Block Elements

Organic Chemistry

O1 Hydrocarbons

O2 Some Functional Groups

O3 More Functional Groups

O4 Large Molecules

Physical Chemistry

P1 The Gaseous State

P2 Equilibrium I: Principles

P3 Equilibrium II: Acids and Bases

P4 Intermolecular Forces and Solvation

P5 Chemical Kinetics

P6 Equilibrium III: Redox Reactions

ROUTES THROUGH ILPAC

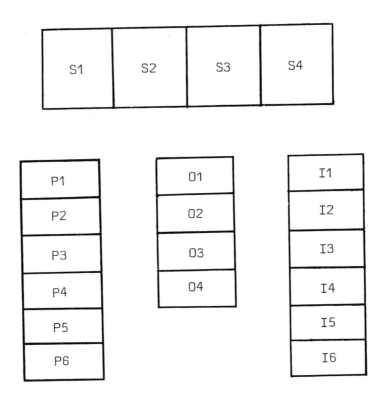

Units S1, S2, S3 and S4 constitute an essential 'starting block' to be completed before starting any other Units.

Thereafter, the order within each Physical, Inorganic and Organic series (P, I and O) should be largely followed, but the three series should normally be 'interwoven' as shown in the three examples below.

P1 →I1 →P2 →O1 →I2 →I3 →P3 →O2 →P4 →I4 →P5 →O3 →P6 →I5 →I6 →O4

I1 →P1 →I2 →O1 →I3 →P2 →I4 →P3 →O2 →P4 →O3 →P5 →P6 →I5 →I6 →O4

O1 →P1 →I1 →P2 →I2 →P3 →O2 →I3 →I4 →P4 →P5 →O3 →P6 →I5 →O4 →I6

These are, of course, just three of the many possible routes through ILPAC.

Notes on variation of order

P6 (Redox Reactions) should be done before I5 (Transition Elements).
P3 (Acids and Bases) should be done before O2 (Some Functional Groups).

P1 (Gaseous State) can be delayed provided that partial pressures are dealt with before P2 (Equilibrium I) and P4 (Intermolecular Forces and Solvation). Also, the Boltzmann distribution which is included in P1, should be dealt with before P5 (Chemical Kinetics).

P5 (Chemical Kinetics) can be brought forward, subject to the note under P1.

ILPAC VIDEO-PROGRAMMES

The following video-programmes have been produced to accompany the ILPAC Units. Although their use is not essential, it does add variety to the course and the visual aspect is often helpful. In some cases, more than one programme appears on a single tape; this is indicated by letters after the titles. The final column shows the Unit(s) for which each programme is considered useful.

ILEA schools may hire or purchase video-tapes from the Learning Materials Service. Outside the ILEA, tapes are available from CFL Vision, Chalfont Grove, Gerrards Cross, Bucks., SL9 8TN (02-407-4111).

Title	Duration (mins)	Unit(s)
Preparing a standard solution (A)	18.58	S1
Performing a titration (A)	25.59	S1
Instrumental techniques	29.22	S2 S4 O3 O4
Ionization energy (B)	9.59	S2
The hydrogen spectrum (C)	16.46	S2
Using a heat of combustion apparatus - glass (D)	12.49	S3
Using a heat of combustion apparatus - aluminium (D)	12.43	S3
Molecules and models	20.03	S4
Identifying unknown substances	40.19	I1 I2 O2 O3
The halogens	38.06	I2
Preparation of aluminium chloride (B)	9.41	I3
Chlorides and oxides (B)	28.20	I3
Group IV elements (to be produced)	-	I4
Transition metals	29.54	I5
Carbon - the key to organic chemistry (E)	19.20	O1 I4
Organic techniques 1 ⎫	28.54	O2
Organic techniques 2 ⎬ Titles slightly amended	34.02	O3
Organic techniques 3 ⎭ in CFL catalogue	33.40	O4
Volumes of reacting gases (D)	26.35	P1
The distribution of molecular speeds (E)	9.29	P1 P5
Equilibrium	31.20	P2
The hydrogen electrode (C)	25.46	P3 P6
Reaction kinetics	46.22	P5
Redox reactions	52.27	P6

SYMBOLS USED IN ILPAC UNITS

 Reading

 Exercise

 Test

 'A' Level question

 'A' Level part question

 'A' Level question Special paper

 Worked example

 Teacher-marked exercise

 Revealing exercise

 Discussion

 Computer programme

 Experiment

 Video programme

 Film loop

 Model-making

INTERNATIONAL HAZARD SYMBOLS

 Harmful

 Flammable

 Corrosive

 Toxic

 Explosive

 Oxidising

 Radioactive

INTRODUCTION

In this first Unit we help you to consolidate some of the ideas about the mole which you have already met in your pre-A-level course.

In Level One we begin by considering relative masses and then develop the concept of the mole as the unit amount of substance. We use the mole concept in stoichiometric calculations to determine how much material is used in a chemical reaction and how to find the empirical formula of a compound.

In Level Two we extend the concept of stoichiometry to reactions in solution and show you how to apply it in a variety of titrations.

There are five experiments in this Unit, as well as some practical exercises involving the weighing of coins.

We have inserted some paragraphs in a different typeface, like the one which follows this, into the first two Units. These are to explain the purpose of the various sections and activities and to help you to use the ILPAC study programme most effectively.

There are two ILPAC videoprogrammes designed to accompany this Unit. Their use is not essential, but you should try to see them at the appropriate time if they are available.

Preparing a standard solution

Performing a titration

At the beginning of every Unit, we list, under the heading PRE-KNOWLEDGE, some abilities which we assume you have and which you will need later in the Unit. Read the list and revise any topics if you think it necessary; or, if you think you have not covered a topic at all, ask your teacher.

Then do the PRE-TEST. From the results, your teacher can tell whether you need any further revision before you begin Level One.

PRE-KNOWLEDGE

Before you start work on this Unit you should be able to:

(1) express numbers in standard form;

(2) multiply and divide numbers expressed in standard form;

(3) state whether a given formula refers to an atom, an ion or a molecule;

(4) identify and name pieces of common laboratory glassware;

(5) write the empirical formula of a compound given its molecular formula

PRE-TEST

To find out whether you are ready to start Level One, try the following test, which is based on the pre-knowledge items. You should not spend more than 30 minutes on this test. Hand your answers to your teacher for marking.

PRE-TEST

1. Numbers written in the form 1.7×10^9 and 9.26×10^{-5} are said to be written in standard form.

    Express in standard form the following numbers:

    (a) 0.000 000 000 500

    (b) 301 000 000 (2)

2. Work out the following, without using a calculator:

    (a) $\dfrac{10^7}{10^2}$ (b) $\dfrac{10^9}{10^{-9}}$ (c) $\dfrac{1.3 \times 10^{12}}{2.6 \times 10^{23}}$ (d) $\dfrac{1.0 \times 10^{-6}}{5.0 \times 10^{-6}}$ (4)

3. The mass of a hydrogen atom is 1.67×10^{-24} g,

    the mass of a carbon atom is 1.99×10^{-23} g,

    the mass of an oxygen atom is 2.66×10^{-23} g and

    the mass of a sodium atom is 3.82×10^{-23} g.

    Calculate the following ratios:

    (a) $\dfrac{\text{mass of a carbon atom}}{\text{mass of a hydrogen atom}}$

    (b) $\dfrac{\text{mass of an oxygen atom}}{\text{mass of a hydrogen atom}}$

    (c) $\dfrac{\text{mass of a sodium atom}}{\text{mass of a hydrogen atom}}$ (3)

4. Do the following calculation, expressing your answer in standard form:

    $$\dfrac{50\ 000\ 000 \times 0.000\ 000\ 000\ 000\ 6}{1.5}$$ (1)

5. Identify each of the following as 'an atom', 'an ion' or 'a molecule'.

    (a) Na   (c) O^{2-} (e) SO_4^{2-}

    (b) F_2 (d) O   (f) IO_3^- (6)

(continued overleaf)

3

6. Name each of the following common pieces of laboratory equipment. Choose your answers from the following list.

    burette   volumetric flask
    beaker   limpette
    conical flask   measuring cylinder
    evaporating dish   pipette
    filter funnel

(a)

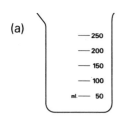

(b)

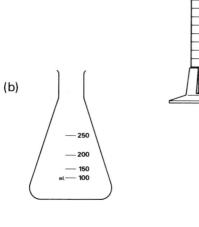

(c)

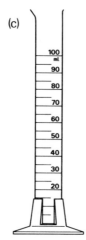

(d)

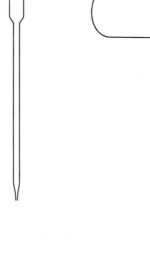

(e)

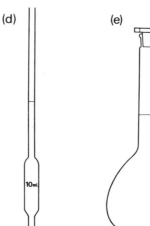

(f)

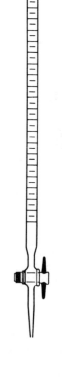

(6)

7. What is the empirical formula of:

(a) propene, C_3H_6

(b) hydrogen peroxide, H_2O_2

(c) ethanoic acid, CH_3CO_2H

(3)

(Total 25 marks)

4

LEVEL ONE

In the early part of this Unit, we want to develop the idea of relative mass of atoms. First, we clarify what we mean by 'relative mass'.

RELATIVE MASS

The mass of any object expressed in any unit is measured relative to some standard. For example, the universal standard of mass is a block of platinum-iridium alloy, called the standard kilogram, which is kept in France at Sèvres, near Paris.

If you buy five kilograms of potatoes, you have five times the mass of the standard kilogram. There are two ways of expressing this:

   'The mass of the potatoes is 5 kg.'

   'The relative mass of the potatoes on the kilogram scale is 5.'

Now you can apply the idea of relative mass to atoms.

Relative Atomic Mass

Atoms are so small that their masses expressed in grams are difficult to work with. Some examples are listed in Table 1.

Table 1

Element	Average mass of an atom/g
H	1.67355×10^{-24}
He	6.64605×10^{-24}
Li	1.15217×10^{-23}
C	1.99436×10^{-23}
O	2.65659×10^{-23}
Na	3.81730×10^{-23}
Ar	6.63310×10^{-23}
U	3.95233×10^{-22}

However, the mass of an atom expressed as relative atomic mass (R.A.M.) is much more manageable.

To develop this idea, you carry out a series of coin-weighing exercises. You use coins, which can be counted and weighed individually, and develop an analogy with atoms, which cannot be counted.

We include these coin-weighing exercises in order to:

(a)   show that any specified object can be the basis of a standard of mass;

(b)   show how the relative mass changes as the standard changes;

(c)   illustrate, by analogy, the different standards for scales of relative atomic mass - the hydrogen scale, the oxygen scale and the carbon-12 scale.

You should not spend more than 2-3 hours on these exercises.

The objectives now follow. These tell you in precise language what you should accomplish in the following section. If there are words which are unfamiliar to you, do not worry; you should understand their meaning by the end of the section.

Objectives. When you have finished this section you should be able to:

(1)   calculate the masses of coins relative to a chosen standard, given the defined standard;

(2)   express the masses of coins in a variety of units.

The first exercise is a practical one. You need access to an accurate balance, and some coins.

Exercise 1   Collect as many contemporary British coins of each kind (½p, 1p, 2p, 5p, 10p) as you can. Weigh a group of each kind to the nearest 0.01 g and calculate the average mass of each of the denominations to the nearest 0.001 g.

In your file, make a copy of Results Table 1 and enter your results in it.

Results Table 1

Coin	[1]Number of coins	[2]Total mass/g	[3]Average mass/g
½p			
1p			
2p			
5p			
10p			

(There is a set of specimen results on page 57)

You can calculate the relative mass of each of the coins on scales different from the gram scale by using the expression:

$$\text{relative mass of coin} = \frac{\text{average mass of coin}}{\text{mass of standard}}$$

We must now pick a suitable standard for comparison. We suggest the ½p coin because it is the lightest of all the coins.

In the next exercise, you determine the mass of each coin relative to the average mass of the ½p coin.

Exercise 2   (a) In your file, make a copy of Results Table 2.
                  Fill in column 1 from Results Table 1.

              (b) Define a unit of mass, the HCU (for half-penny
                  coin unit). Let one HCU equal the average mass
                  of a ½p coin as you determined it in Exercise 1.
                  In your notes write:

                       1.00 HCU = _____ g

                  and fill in the value.

              (c) Calculate the relative mass of each type of coin on the HCU
                  scale using the expression:

$$\text{relative mass of coin} = \frac{\text{average mass of coin}}{\text{mass of HCU}}$$

                  Enter your results in column 2. (Columns 3 and 4 will not
                  be used until Exercises 3 and 4.)

7

Results Table 2

Coin	1 Average mass/g	Relative mass		
		2 Mass /HCU	3 Mass /OCU	4 Mass /CCU
½p				
1p				
2p				
5p				
10p				

(There is a set of specimen results on page   57)

You should notice that the relative masses are all larger than 1 (except, of course, for the ½p coin). We have ensured this by choosing the lightest coin as standard.

In the same way, an atom of hydrogen was the chosen standard for the first atomic mass scale because hydrogen is the lightest element. It was convenient to have all relative atomic masses greater than (or equal to) 1.

Hydrogen was abandoned as a standard for a number of reasons, one being that so few elements combine with it. A new standard, based on oxygen, was chosen.

In the next exercise, we similarly abandon the ½p coin as the standard and replace it with a standard based on the 1p coin.

Since the mass of a 1p coin is about twice the mass of a ½p coin, we let the new standard equal one half the average mass of a 1p coin. This keeps the relative mass of the lightest coin about 1, which conveniently avoids fractions.

Exercise 3   (a) Define a second unit of mass, the OCU (for one penny coin unit). Using the data in Results Table 1, write in your notes:

Average mass of 1p coin = _____ g

1.000 OCU = ½ x average mass of 1p coin

1.000 OCU = _____ g

(b) Calculate the relative mass of each type of coin using the expression:

$$\text{relative mass of coin} = \frac{\text{average mass of coin}}{\text{mass of OCU}}$$

Record the values in column 3 of Results Table 2.

(A set of specimen results is on page   57)

8

Compare the values in columns 2 and 3 of Results Table 2. Notice that in both OCU and HCU scales, the masses are in the ratio of about 1:2:4 for the ½p, 1p and 2p coins.

After the adoption of the oxygen scale, scientists discovered that oxygen is a mixture of isotopes*. The composition of the mixture varies slightly and so, therefore, does the average mass of an oxygen atom which was used as a standard. It became necessary to adopt a new standard which does not vary.

The new standard is based on the mass of the most abundant isotope of carbon, carbon-12 (^{12}C). Similarly, in the next exercise, we adopt a new standard - based on the mass of a freshly-minted 2p piece. Unlike coins already in use which may be heavier due to dirt sticking to them, or lighter due to wear, a newly-minted coin has a known mass.

Since the mass of a 2p coin is about four times the mass of a ½p coin, we can avoid fractions by letting the new standard equal one quarter the mass of a newly-minted 2p coin. This keeps the relative mass of the lightest coin about 1.

*Isotopes are atoms of an element which have almost identical properties except that their masses differ due to having different numbers of neutrons (see the next Unit: Atomic Structure).

Exercise 4   According to the Royal Mint, the mass of a newly-minted 2p piece is 7.128 g. So we define a third unit, the CCU (copper coin unit), as one quarter the mass of a newly-minted 2p coin.

$$1.000 \text{ CCU} = \tfrac{1}{4} \times 7.128 \text{ g}$$

$$1.000 \text{ CCU} = 1.782 \text{ g}$$

Using the defined value for the CCU, calculate the relative masses for column 4 of Results Table 2.

(A set of specimen results is on page 57)

Now you can apply the same ideas to calculations involving atoms rather than coins.

The relative atomic mass scale

You have just completed a series of exercises using coins to illustrate how relative mass changes as the choice of standard changes. Next, you do a similar exercise using masses of atoms instead of coins, in which you calculate relative atomic masses on the hydrogen, oxygen and carbon-12 scales.

Objective.   When you have finished this section you should be able to:

(3)   define relative atomic mass in terms of carbon-12.

Exercise 5   Use the values in Table 1 to calculate atomic
              masses relative to

(a) hydrogen,

(b) oxygen,

(c) carbon-12

in a manner similar to the way you calculated relative masses of
coins. Enter your values into a copy of Results Table 3. Some
values are included as a check. (The mass of an atom of
carbon-12 = 1.99252 x 10^{-23} g.)

Results Table 3

Element	Relative Atomic Mass (R.A.M.)		
	H scale	O scale	^{12}C scale
H	1.00000		1.00790
He		4.00276	
Li	6.88459		
C			12.01110
O		16.0000	
Na	22.8096		
Ar		39.9496	
U			238.030

(Answers on page 57)

In most of your A-level work, you use relative atomic masses expressed to
three significant figures, e.g. He = 4.00, O = 16.0, Ar = 39.9, U = 238.
To this degree of precision, the oxygen scale and the carbon-12 scale can
be regarded as the same, but you should never use the hydrogen scale
because it differs so much from the others.

For more accurate work, the difference between the oxygen and carbon-12 scales
is important and in 1961, IUPAC (the International Union of Pure and Applied
Chemistry) adopted the carbon-12 scale as standard. These values are quoted
in all publications since that date.

You will learn more about the methods of measuring relative atomic mass in
the next Unit. In this Unit you use relative atomic mass in calculations
involving amounts of substance.

AMOUNT

You have already learned to give special scientific meanings to familiar
everyday words like 'element' and 'compound'. Now you look more closely at
the familiar word 'amount'.

'Amount' is another physical quantity like mass, volume, length, time, etc. It gives us an alternative, and very useful, way of expressing how much there is of a substance.

We can express how much there is of a substance as a mass (by reference to a standard mass), as a volume (by reference to a standard volume), or as an amount (by reference to a standard <u>counting unit</u>).

As with all other physical quantities, an amount is written as a number times an associated unit:

mass = 10.2 kg   time = 42.1 s   temperature = 273 K

length = 0.7 m   volume = 24.2 cm^3 amount = 19 dozen

Calculating amount by weighing

Here is another coin-weighing exercise to illustrate that you can calculate the amount of coins once you define the mass per unit amount. In this case the unit of amount is the dozen.

<u>Objective</u>.   When you have finished this section you should be able to:

(4)   calculate the amount of identical objects given the mass of each object and the mass per unit amount of objects.

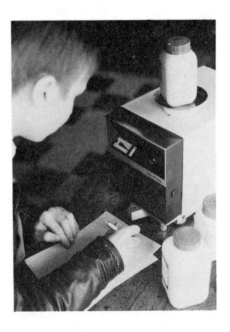

For this exercise you will be given, in separate opaque jars, some ½p, 1p and 2p coins. Simply by weighing, you can calculate the amount of coins in each jar.

<u>Exercise 6</u>   (a) Weigh the jars; subtract the mass of the empty jar (shown on the outside of the jar) and record the mass of the coins in column 1 of a copy of Results Table 4.

Results Table 4

Coin	[1]Total mass of coins in jar/g	[2]Mass per dozen /g doz^{-1}	[3]Amount in jar/doz
½p			
1p			
2p			

(b) Using the average mass of each type of coin (column 3 of Results Table 1) calculate the mass per dozen of each type of coin and fill in column 2. Note the unit, g doz^{-1}.

(c) Calculate the amount in each jar by dividing the mass of coins by the mass per dozen. Fill in column 3. Again, note the unit.

(d) Open the jars and count the number of coins in each jar to check your calculations. Replace all the coins in the correct jar and return them.

(There is a set of specimen results on page 57)

People do count coins by weighing them. For example, if a cashier in a bank is given a bag containing 2p coins which is found to have a mass of 356 g, then she knows that the bag contains 50 coins. If the bag weighs 178 g, then she knows that the bag contains 25 coins, and so on.

We can generalise the results of Exercise 6 in the following expression:

$$\text{amount of objects} = \frac{\text{mass of objects}}{\text{mass per unit amount* of objects}}$$

*By 'unit amount' we mean one dozen, one gross, one ream, etc. You use this idea in the next two exercises.

Throughout the course, you are expected to give the answers to numerical exercises correct to three significant figures (unless otherwise stated). You should see the appendix, page 53, for the use of significant figures in calculations.

Exercise 7   One dozen pencils weighs 45.0 g. Calculate the amount of pencils in a consignment weighing 5625 g.

(Answer on page 57)

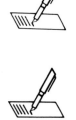

Exercise 8   One gross(144) of paper clips weighs 82.08 g. A sample of paper clips weighs 5.13 x 10^6 g.

(a) Calculate the amount of paper clips (in units of gross) in the sample.

(b) How many paper clips are there in the sample?

(Answers on page 57)

Amount of substance - the mole

As objects get smaller, the number in a unit amount gets larger; for example, we buy a pair of socks, a dozen eggs and a ream (500 sheets) of paper.

In counting atoms we also need a convenient unit, large enough to be seen and handled. Since atoms are so small, there are a great many of them in a convenient unit.

Objectives. When you have finished this section you should be able to:

(5)   define (a) the mole,

               (b) molar mass;

(6)   quote the value of the Avogadro Constant to three significant figures.

The counting unit for atoms, molecules and ions is the mole (abbreviation: mol). It is defined as the amount of substance that contains as many elementary particles as there are atoms in 0.012 kg (12 g) of carbon-12. You must learn this definition.

The mass of an atom of carbon-12 is 1.99252×10^{-23} g. So the number of atoms in 12 g of carbon-12 is given by

$$\frac{12 \text{ g}}{1.99252 \times 10^{-23} \text{ g}} = 6.02252 \times 10^{23}$$

Note that in this context, 12 is taken to be an integer and it does not therefore limit the significant figures in the answer to two.

The Avogadro constant (symbol: L) relates the number of particles to the amount. It is represented as L = 6.02252 x 10^{23} mol^{-1} or, to three significant figures,

$$L = 6.02 \times 10^{23} \text{ mol}^{-1}$$

The following examples try to convey the magnitude of the Avogadro constant:

If you had 6.02 x 10^{23} tiny grains of pollen they would cover the City of London to a depth of 1 mile.

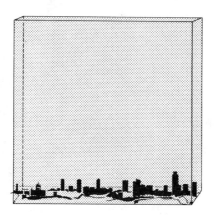

Fig. 2.

6.02 x 10^{23} marshmallows spread over the United States of America would yield a blanket of marshmallows more than 600 miles deep!

Computers can count about 10 million times per second. At this rate 6.02 x 10^{23} counts would require almost 2 billion years.

A similar example is included in the next exercise.

Exercise 9   A 5 cm^3 spoon can hold 1.67 x 10^{23} molecules of water.

    (a) How long would it take to remove them one at a time at a rate of one molecule per second?

    (b) How many years is this?

(Answer on page   57)

Molar Mass

The mass per unit amount of substance is called its molar mass (symbol: M) and is the mass per mole of that substance. We usually use the unit: g mol^{-1}

Objective.   When you have finished this section, you should be able to:

(7) calculate the molar mass of a substance, given its formula and a table of relative atomic masses.

The molar mass of an element is the mass per mole. It follows from the definition of the mole that the molar mass of carbon is 12.0 g mol^{-1}. Similarly, since the relative atomic mass of uranium is 238, M = 238 g mol^{-1}.

The term molar mass applies not only to elements in the atomic state but also to all chemical species - atoms, molecules, ions, etc.

For ethane, the molar mass is calculated from its formula, C_2H_6, which indicates that one molecule contains two atoms of carbon and six atoms of hydrogen. The relative atomic masses are: C = 12.0, H = 1.0. The relative mass of a molecule on the same scale is therefore given by:

$$\boxed{C_2H_6}$$

$$(2 \times 12.0) + (6 \times 1.0) = 30$$

Thus, the relative molecular mass of ethane is 30.0 and its molar mass, M = 30.0 g mol^{-1}.

There are two important points which you must bear in mind when dealing with amounts of substances:

1. You must specify exactly what entity the amount refers to. The phrase '1 mol of chlorine', for instance, has two possible meanings because it does not specify whether it refers to atoms or molecules. To avoid confusion, you must always specify the entity, either by formula or in words:

    1.0 mol of Cl   or   one mole of chlorine atoms

    1.0 mol of Cl_2 or   one mole of chlorine molecules

2. By weighing out the same number of grams as the relative atomic mass or the relative molecular mass (whether atoms, molecules or ions) you have measured out one mole, i.e. 6.02×10^{23} atoms, molecules or ions.

The following two exercises test your understanding of these concepts and give you practice in using your data book.

You will refer frequently to your data book throughout this course so you must learn how to use it. In the next exercise you use your data book to calculate molar masses. Turn to the index of the data book and find the page reference(s) for either relative atomic mass or molar mass of elements. If there is more than one reference, look them up to see which is most convenient.

You nearly always use approximate values, so a table of precise values may be confusing. Is it easier to have the elements listed alphabetically or by atomic number?

Always look carefully at the headings of columns in tables of data and read any accompanying notes to make sure that the data really is what you want and that you quote the correct units.

Exercise 10   Using your data book, calculate the molar masses of

    (a) ammonia, NH_3,

    (b) calcium bromide, $CaBr_2$,

    (c) phosphoric(V) acid, H_3PO_4,

    (d) sodium sulphate-10-water, $Na_2SO_4 \cdot 10H_2O$

    (Answers on page 57)

Exercise 11   What is the mass of 1.00 mol of

    (a) chlorine atoms,

    (b) chlorine, Cl_2,

    (c) phosphorus, P,

    (d) phosphorus, P_4,

    (e) iodide ions, I^-.

    (Answers on page 58)

Amount Calculations

Objectives.   At the end of this section you should be able to:

(8)   calculate the amount of a substance given its mass and molar mass;

(9)   calculate the number of particles in a given amount.

In Exercise 6 you determined the amount of coins in the jar by using the expression:

$$\text{amount of coins} = \frac{\text{mass}}{\text{mass per dozen}}$$

In science, the amount of substance in a given sample is similarly defined as the mass of the sample divided by the mass per mole (i.e. the molar mass):

$$\boxed{\text{amount of substance} = \frac{\text{mass}}{\text{molar mass}}}$$

The symbol for amount is n and, therefore, in symbols:

$$\boxed{n = \frac{m}{M}}$$

The following worked example shows you how to use this expression in mole calculations.

Reminder: the unit for amount is mole, for mass is gram, and for molar mass is grams per mole (abbreviation: $g\ mol^{-1}$).

Throughout the course, we explain calculations by Worked Examples. Read through the Worked Example carefully, then try the exercises which follow it. If you are unable to do a particular problem, go through the Worked Example again. If this fails, look at the method in the answer, then try again. If this does not help, ask your teacher.

Don't be casual over calculations – write out every step of the solution and be sure to include units. This will ensure that you end up with the correct units in the answer. In an examination, a clearly-set-out method not only gains you marks if your answer is wrong due to mathematical error but also helps you do the problem correctly.

<u>Worked Example.</u> A sample of carbon weighs 180 g. What amount of carbon is present?

<u>Solution</u>

Calculate the amount by substituting into the key expression:

$$n = \frac{m}{M}$$

where m = 180 g and M = 12.0 g mol^{-1}

$$\therefore n = \frac{m}{M} = \frac{180 \text{ g}}{12.0 \text{ g mol}^{-1}} = \boxed{15.0 \text{ mol}}$$

At this point you should make sure that you are not using formula in a mechanical way but understand what you are doing. So, here is an alternative method which relies on first principles. YOU SHOULD NEVER SUBSTITUTE INTO AN EXPRESSION WITHOUT FIRST UNDERSTANDING HOW IT WAS DERIVED OR DEFINED.

<u>Alternative solution</u>

1. Write down the mass of 1.00 mol of the substance in the form of a sentence:

    12.0 g is the mass of 1.00 mol of carbon.

2. Scale down to the amount of carbon in 1.00 g by dividing by 12.0 throughout

    $\frac{12.0}{12.0}$ g is the mass of $\frac{1.00}{12.0}$ mol of carbon

3. Scale up to the amount of carbon in 180 g by multiplying by 180 throughout

    $180 \times \frac{12.0}{12.0}$ g is the mass of $180 \times \frac{1.00}{12.0}$ mol of carbon

    i.e. 180 g is the mass of 15.0 mol of carbon

    $\therefore$ the amount of carbon in 180 g = $\boxed{15.0 \text{ mol}}$

Now attempt the following exercises. (We use the method of substituting into the expression in our answers, largely because it takes up less space. You can try the 'sentence method' if you get stuck.)

Exercise 12   Calculate the amount in each of the following:

(a) 30.0 g of oxygen molecules, O_2,

(b) 31.0 g of phosphorus molecules, P_4,

(c) 50.0 g of calcium carbonate, $CaCO_3$.

(Answers on page 58)

You must also be prepared for questions which ask you to calculate the mass of substance in a given amount. To do this in the following exercises, use the expression:

$$n = \frac{m}{M} \quad \text{in the form} \quad m = nM$$

Exercise 13   Calculate the mass of each of the following:

(a) 1.00 mol of hydrogen, H_2,

(b) 0.500 mol of sodium chloride, $NaCl$,

(c) 0.250 mol of carbon dioxide, CO_2.

(Answers on page 58)

Exercise 14   A sample of ammonia, NH_3, weighs 1.00g.

(a) What amount of ammonia is contained in this sample?

(b) What mass of sulphur dioxide, SO_2, contains the same number of molecules as are in 1.00 g of ammonia?

(Answers on page 58)

We now consider another type of amount calculation.

Calculating the number of particles in a given amount

Sometimes you are required to calculate the number of particles in a given amount of substance. This is easy because you know the number of particles in 1.00 mol (6.02×10^{23}). Use the expression:

$$\boxed{N = nL}$$

where N = the number of particles, n = the amount, L = the Avogadro constant.

Exercise 15   Calculate the number of atoms in:

(a) 18.0 g of carbon, C,

(b) 18.0 g of copper, Cu,

(c) 7.20 g of sulphur, S_8.

(Answers on page 58)

Exercise 16   Calculate the number of molecules in:

        (a) 1.00 g of ammonia, NH_3,

        (b) 3.28 g of sulphur dioxide, SO_2,

        (c) 7.20 g of sulphur, S_8.

        (Answers on page **58**)

Exercise 17   Calculate the number of ions present in:

        (a) 0.500 mol of sodium chloride, NaCl (Na^+, Cl^-),

        (b) 14.6 g of sodium chloride, NaCl,

        (c) 18.5 g of calcium chloride, $CaCl_2$.

        (Answers on page **59**)

The Avogadro constant is an important quantity, and at least twenty different methods have been devised to measure or calculate it. The next experiment illustrates a simple method which is capable of giving an approximate value.

Make sure that you have time to do the experiment and that your teacher knows that you are about to do it. Also make sure you understand the purpose of the experiment; this is stated in the aim. The introduction gives information needed for the experiment. Pay attention to any HAZARD WARNINGS — these advise you on the dangers of handling certain chemicals. If you are told to wear safety spectacles or use a fume cupboard, then you MUST do so. If laboratory time is scarce, complete the experiment before doing calculations; then you can write up the experiment at home. We now give you some advice on writing up experiments.

WRITING UP EXPERIMENTS

We suggest you write up experiments carefully after completing them, using most of the headings we use in the Unit.

Title and Aim.   These will be the same as in the Unit.

Procedure.   Our instructions have to be very detailed: your account should be much briefer, more like our introduction but with enough detail added to remind you of the method.

Results Tables.   These are designed to help you record data in a form which you can use easily. Get used to recording results clearly as you work — scribbled figures on scraps of paper can be confusing even if you don't lose them! Your teacher may be able to give you duplicated blank tables.

Calculations.   You must include enough explanation to enable you to follow the calculations when you revise. A couple of lines of scribbled figures with no indication of method is quite useless. Our specimen calculations are a good guide.

Objective. When you have completed this experiment you should be able to:

(10) calculate the Avogadro Constant from data obtained in the monomolecular layer experiment.

EXPERIMENT 1
Determining the Avogadro Constant

Aim

The purpose of this experiment is to estimate the value of the Avogadro constant and to compare this estimate with the accepted value.

Introduction

When a solution of oleic acid, $C_{17}H_{33}CO_2H$, in pentane is dropped on to water, the pentane evaporates leaving behind a layer of oleic acid one molecule thick. For this reason, this experiment has been called 'The Monomolecular Layer Experiment'.

You use a loop of hair or thread to contain the oleic acid and to give a measure of the surface area. By making certain assumptions about the shape of the molecule and its alignment on the surface, you can get a reasonably accurate value for the Avogadro constant.

The experiment has two parts. In the first, you calibrate the pipette. This gives the volume of one drop of solution. In the second part you determine how many drops of solution are required to just fill the loop with a layer of oleic acid molecules. Then we lead you, step by step, through the calculation.

Requirements

measuring cylinder, 10 cm³
teat pipette and adaptor (for small drops)
trough
human hair or cotton thread, 40 - 50 cm
scissors
petroleum jelly or Vaseline
oleic acid solution in pentane (0.05 cm³ of oleic acid per dm³)-------

Hazard Warning

Pentane is highly flammable.

Therefore you MUST:

KEEP THE STOPPER ON THE BOTTLE WHEN NOT IN USE:

KEEP THE LIQUID AWAY FROM FLAMES.

Procedure

1. Fill the teat pipette with oleic acid solution and deliver it drop by drop into the 10 cm³ measuring cylinder. Count the number of drops which must be delivered from the pipette to reach the 1 cm³ mark. Enter your value in a copy of Results Table 5.

   Results Table 5

Number of drops to deliver 1 cm³ of solution	Number of drops delivered to make monomolecular layer	Diameter of monomolecular layer/cm

2. Tie the hair or cotton thread in a loop. Use a reef-knot (Fig. 3), rather than an overhand knot, so that the loop will make a flat circle. Cut the ends as close to the knot as possible. Hair is preferred because it does not need greasing but if you are using thread, thoroughly but lightly grease it with petroleum jelly. It is most important that no part of the thread escapes greasing. Run the knotted thread through your fingers several times before wiping off the excess.

Fig. 3.

3. Fill the trough with water and float the loop on it, making sure that the entire circumference is in contact with the surface. Look very carefully for 'bridges' or submerged loops and move them into the surface with a clean glass rod or a pencil point.

21

4. Using the same pipette, add the oleic acid solution dropwise to the
    middle of the loop until it is filled. At first you will probably see
    the loop expand to a circle and then retract again.
    Before the loop is filled, it 'gives' when you push it gently from the
    outside with a pencil. (Fig. 4)
    When the loop is filled, it will slide across the surface, only denting
    very slightly when pushed gently with the pencil. (Fig. 5)

Fig. 4.   Fig. 5.

    Count the number of drops required to fill the loop and record this in a
    copy of Results Table 5.

5. Measure the diameter of the loop and complete Results Table 5.

6. If you have time, repeat the whole procedure. However, you must use a
    fresh hair or thread, and wash out the trough thoroughly to obtain a
    clean surface.

Calculation

1. Calculate the volume of 1 drop delivered from the teat pipette using the
    value in column one of Results Table 5.

        Volume of 1 drop = _____ cm³

2. Calculate the volume of oleic acid in 1 drop of solution delivered from
    the teat pipette.

    Remember that 1000 cm³ of this solution contains 0.05 cm³ of oleic acid.

        Volume of oleic acid in 1 drop = _____ cm³

3. Calculate the volume of oleic acid delivered to make the monomolecular
    layer; i.e. the volume of oleic acid in 1 drop x the number of drops
    required.

        Volume of oleic acid in monolayer = _____ cm³

4. Calculate the surface area of the oleic acid layer.

        Area = $\pi d^2/4$ = _____ cm²

5. You know the volume of oleic acid (from 3) and the surface area it covers
    (from 4). It is a simple matter to calculate the thickness of the layer
    because volume = area x thickness.

Fig. 6.
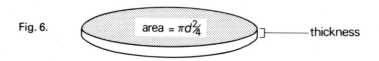
area = $\pi d^2/4$ ———— thickness

        Thickness = _____ cm

22

6. Calculate the volume of one molecule of oleic acid by assuming it is a cube, with sides equal to the thickness of the layer.

    Volume of one molecule = _____ cm^3

7. Calculate the volume of a mole of oleic acid given that its density is 0.890 g cm^{-3} and its molar mass is 282 g mol^{-1}

    Volume of 1 mol of oleic acid = _____ cm^3

8. Divide the volume of one mole by the volume of one molecule to determine the Avogadro constant.

    L = _____ mol^{-1}

(There is a set of specimen results on page 59)

Questions

1. Suggest some sources of error in this experiment which account for the discrepancy between the value of L you obtained and the accepted value of $L = 6.02 \times 10^{23}$ mol^{-1}.

2. Which of the values you used in your calculations is subject to the greatest error?

3. Pentane is not the only liquid that can be used in this experiment. Suggest four properties which a suitable substitute must have.

(Answers on page 60)

We now consider how we can use the mole concept to calculate how much of one substance will react with a given amount of another - this is called stoichiometry and is one of the main reasons why the mole concept is so important in the study of chemistry.

STOICHIOMETRY

Stoichiometry (pronounced stoy-key-om-i-tree) in its broadest sense includes all the quantitative relationships in chemical reactions. It has to do with how much of one substance will react with another. A chemical equation such as

$$N_2(g) + 3H_2(g) \rightarrow 2NH_3(g)$$

is a kind of chemical balance sheet; it states that one mole of nitrogen reacts with three moles of hydrogen to yield two moles of ammonia. (It does not tell us about the rate of the reaction or the conditions necessary to bring it about.) The numbers 1, 3 and 2 are called the stoichiometric coefficients. Such an equation is an essential starting point for many experiments and calculations; it tells us the proportions in which the substances react and in which the products are formed.

Objective.   When you have finished this section you should be able to:

(11)   do simple reacting mass calculations based on a given chemical equation,
       i.e. stoichiometric calculations.

We start with a worked example.

Worked Example   What mass of iodine will react completely with
                  10.0 g of aluminium?

This problem is a little more complicated than those you have done previously,
because it involves several steps. Each step is very simple, but you may not
immediately see where to start. Before we present a detailed solution, let
us look at a way of approaching multi-step problems. Even if you find this
problem easy, the approach may be useful to you in more difficult problems.
We suggest that you ask yourself three questions:

1.   What do I know?   In this case, the answer should be:

     (a)   the equation for the reaction;

     (b)   the mass of aluminium.

In some problems you may be given the equation; in this one, you are expected
to write it down from your general chemical knowledge. In nearly every
problem about a reaction, the equation provides vital information.

2.   What can I get from what I know?

     (a)   From the equation, I can find the ratio of reacting amounts.

     (b)   From the mass of aluminium, I can calculate the amount, provided I
           look up the molar mass.

3.   Can I now see how to get the final answer?

     In most cases the answer will be 'Yes', but you may have to ask the second
     question again, now that you know more than you did at the start.

     (a)   From the amount of aluminium and the ratio of reacting amounts, I can
           calculate the amount of iodine.

     (b)   From the amount of iodine, I can get the mass, using the molar mass.

     Instead of writing answers to these questions, you can summarise your
     thinking in a flow diagram.

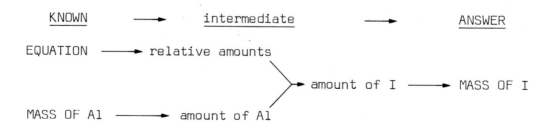

An alternative strategy is to work backwards from the answer towards the given information, or you may use a combination of both strategies, meeting up in the middle. In any case, the steps you use will probably be the same, although the order in which you take them may be different.

Now we go through each step, using the first strategy, and doing the necessary calculations.

Solution

1. Write the balanced equation for the reaction:

$$2Al(s) + 3I_2(s) \rightarrow 2AlI_3(s)$$

This equation tells us that 2 mol of Al reacts with 3 mol of I_2; so we write the ratio:

$$\frac{\text{amount of Al}}{\text{amount of } I_2} = \frac{2}{3}$$

2. Calculate the amount of aluminium using the expression:

$$n = \frac{m}{M}$$

$$\therefore \quad n = \frac{10.0 \text{ g}}{27.0 \text{ g mol}^{-1}} = 0.370 \text{ mol}$$

3. Calculate the amount of iodine which reacts with this amount of aluminium by substituting into the expression based on the equation:

$$\frac{\text{amount of Al}}{\text{amount of } I_2} = \frac{2}{3}$$

$$\therefore \quad \text{amount of } I_2 = \frac{3}{2} \times \text{amount of Al}$$

$$= \frac{3}{2} \times 0.370 \text{ mol} = 0.555 \text{ mol}$$

4. Calculate the mass of iodine from the amount using the expression:

$$n = \frac{m}{M} \quad \text{in the form} \quad m = nM$$

$$\therefore \quad m = nM = 0.555 \text{ mol} \times 254 \text{ g mol}^{-1} = \boxed{141 \text{ g}}$$

Now try some similar problems for yourself.

Exercise 18   (a) What mass of magnesium would react completely with 16.0 g of sulphur?

$$Mg(s) + S(s) \rightarrow MgS(s)$$

(b) What mass of oxygen would be produced by completely decomposing 4.25 g of sodium nitrate, $NaNO_3$?

$$2NaNO_3(s) \rightarrow 2NaNO_2(s) + O_2(g)$$

(Answers on page 60)

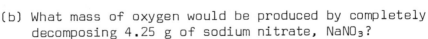

25

Exercise 19   What mass of phosphorus(V) oxide, P_2O_5, would be
               formed by complete oxidation of 4.00 g of phosphorus?

$$4P(s) + 5O_2(g) \rightarrow 2P_2O_5(s)$$

               (Answer on page   60)

Exercise 20   When 0.27 g of aluminium is added to excess
               copper(II) sulphate solution, 0.96 g of copper
               is precipitated. Deduce the equation for the
               reaction which takes place.

               (Answer on page   60)

In the next exercise you have to decide first which one of two reactants is
present in excess.

Exercise 21   A mixture containing 2.80 g of iron and 2.00 g of
               sulphur is heated together. What mass of iron(II)
               sulphide, FeS, is produced?

$$Fe(s) + S(s) \rightarrow FeS(s)$$

               (Answer on page 61)

Another important application of the mole concept is in the calculation of
the empirical formulae of substances.

CALCULATING EMPIRICAL FORMULAE

The empirical formula of a compound is the simplest form of the ratio of the
atoms of different elements in it. The molecular formula tells the actual
number of each kind of atom in a molecule of the substance. For example, the
molecular formula of tetraphosphorus decoxide is P_4O_{10}, whereas its empirical
formula is P_2O_5.

Objective.   When you have finished this section you should be able to:

(12)   calculate the empirical formula of a compound given either

       (a) the masses of constituents in a sample, or

       (b) the composition in terms of the mass percentages of the
           constituents.

Calculating empirical formulae from the masses of constituents

To determine the empirical formula of a compound, we must first calculate the
amount of each substance present in a sample and then calculate the simplest
whole-number ratio of the amounts.

It is convenient to set the results out in tabular form and we suggest that
you use this method. However, in the following Worked Example, we will go
through the procedure step by step, establishing the table as we go.

Worked Example   An 18.3 g sample of a hydrated compound contained
                  4.0 g of calcium, 7.1 g of chlorine and 7.2 g of
                  water only. Calculate its empirical formula.

Solution

1. List the mass of each component and its molar mass. Although water is a
    molecule, in the calculation we treat it in the same way as we do atoms.

	Ca	Cl	H_2O
Mass/g	4.0	7.1	7.2
Molar mass/g mol^{-1}	40.0	35.5	18.0

2. From this information calculate the amount of each substance present using
    the expression. $n = \dfrac{m}{M}$

	Ca	Cl	H_2O
Amount/mol	$\dfrac{4.0}{40.0} = 0.10$	$\dfrac{7.1}{35.5} = 0.20$	$\dfrac{7.2}{18.0} = 0.40$

(For simplicity, we have omitted the units from the calculation - they
cancel anyway.)

This result means that in the given sample there is 0.10 mol of calcium,
0.20 mol of chlorine and 0.40 mol of water.

3. Calculate the <u>relative</u> amount of each substance by dividing each amount
    by the smallest amount.

	Ca	Cl	H_2O
Amount/smallest amount = relative amount	$\dfrac{0.10}{0.10} = 1.0$	$\dfrac{0.20}{0.10} = 2.0$	$\dfrac{0.40}{0.10} = 4.0$

The relative amounts are in the simple ratio 1:2:4.

From this result you can see that the empirical formula is $CaCl_2 \cdot 4H_2O$

To see if you understand this procedure, try Exercise 22.

Exercise 22   A sample of a hydrated compound was analysed and
               found to contain 2.10 g of cobalt, 1.14 g of
               sulphur, 2.28 g of oxygen and 4.50 g of water.
               Calculate its empirical formula.

               (Answer on page 61)

A modification of this type of problem is to determine the ratio of the
amount of water to the amount of anhydrous compound. You have practice in
this type of problem in the next exercise.

Exercise 23   10.00 g of hydrated barium chloride are heated
               until all the water is driven off. The mass of
               anhydrous compound is 8.53 g. Determine the
               value of x in $BaCl_2 \cdot xH_2O$.

(Answer on page 61)

You should be prepared for variations to this type of problem. The following
part of an A-level question illustrates such a variation.

Exercise 24   When 585 mg of the salt $UO(C_2O_4) \cdot 6H_2O$ was left
               in a vacuum desiccator for forty-eight hours,
               the mass changed to 535 mg. What formula would
               you predict for the resulting substance?

(Answers on page 61)

Now look at another way of calculating empirical formula.

Calculating empirical formula from percentage composition by mass

The result of the analysis of a compound may also be given in terms of the
percentage composition by mass. Study the following Worked Example which
deals with this type of problem.

Worked Example   An organic compound was analysed and was found
                   to have the following percentage composition by
                   mass: 48.8% carbon, 13.5% hydrogen and 37.7%
                   nitrogen. Calculate the empirical formula of
                   the compound.

Solution

If we <u>assume</u> the mass of the sample is 100.0 g, we can write immediately the
mass of each substance: 48.8 g of carbon, 13.5 g of hydrogen and 37.7 g of
nitrogen. Then we set up a table as before. The instructions between each
step are omitted this time, but you should check our calculations.

	C	H	N
Mass/g	48.8	13.5	37.7
Molar mass/g mol^{-1}	12.0	1.00	14.0
Amount/mol	4.07	13.5	2.69
$\dfrac{\text{Amount}}{\text{Smallest amount}}$	$\dfrac{4.07}{2.69} = 1.51$	$\dfrac{13.5}{2.69} = 5.02$	$\dfrac{2.69}{2.69} = 1.00$
Simplest ratio of relative amounts	3	10	2

Empirical formula = $C_3H_{10}N_2$

28

In the preceding exercises you 'rounded off' values close to whole numbers in order to get a simple ratio. This is justified because small differences from whole numbers are probably due to experimental errors. Here, however, we cannot justify rounding off 1.51 to 1 or 2, but we can obtain a simple ratio by multiplying the relative amounts by two.

Now attempt the following exercises where you must decide whether to round off or multiply by a factor.

Exercise 25   A compound of carbon, hydrogen and oxygen contains 40.0% carbon, 6.6% hydrogen and 53.4% oxygen. Calculate its empirical formula.

(Answer on page 61)

Exercise 26   Determine the formula of a mineral with the following mass composition: Na = 12.1%, Al = 14.2%, Si = 22.1%, O = 42.1%, H_2O = 9.48%.

(Answer on page 62)

Exercise 27   A 10.00 g sample of a compound contains 3.91 g of carbon, 0.87 g of hydrogen and the remainder is oxygen. Calculate the empirical formula of the compound.

(Answer on page 62)

We now consider how we can use the mole concept for reactions taking place in solution.

AMOUNTS IN SOLUTION

So far we have shown how to calculate amount of substance from the mass of a substance and its molar mass. However, most chemical reactions take place in solution. If we want to know the amount of substance in solution, then we must know the concentration of the solution and its volume.

Objectives.   When you have finished this section you should be able to:

(13)   define concentration;

(14)   explain the term standard solution;

(15)   calculate the concentration of a solution given the amount or mass of solute and the volume of solution;

(16)   calculate the amount or mass of solute in a given volume of solution of known concentration.

Concentration of solution

We express the concentration of a solution as the amount of solute dissolved in a given volume of solution;   i.e.

$$\text{concentration} = \frac{\text{amount}}{\text{volume}} \quad \text{or, in symbols,} \quad \boxed{c = \frac{n}{V}}$$

Normally, we measure:

amount in mol, and volume in dm^3, so the usual unit of concentration is <u>$mol\ dm^{-3}$</u>.

Standard solutions

A standard solution is one of known concentration. We can 'know' the concentration either by preparing the solution according to a given recipe or by analysing it.

Let us suppose we dissolve 0.15 mol (27.0 g) of glucose, $C_6H_{12}O_6$, in enough water to make 1.00 dm^3 of solution. Then its concentration is given as $c = 0.15\ mol\ dm^{-3}$.

The letter M is sometimes used as an abbreviation for $mol\ dm^{-3}$, but you should <u>only</u> use it in conjunction with a formula. For example, 0.0100 M NaOH means a solution of sodium hydroxide, NaOH, having a concentration of 0.0100 $mol\ dm^{-3}$.

In this section, we go through the main types of problems you are likely to meet which involve solutions. For each one, read the Worked Example, then try the exercises which follow it.

Calculating concentration from volume and amount

<u>Worked Example.</u>   Calculate the concentration of a solution which is made by dissolving 0.500 mol of sodium hydroxide NaOH in 200 cm^3 of solution.

<u>Solution</u>

Calculate the concentration by substituting into the key expression:

$$c = \frac{n}{V}$$

where n = 0.500 mol and $V = \left(\frac{200}{1000}\right) cm^3$

$$c = \frac{n}{V} = \frac{0.500\ mol}{0.200\ dm^3} = \boxed{2.50\ mol\ dm^{-3}}$$

Now attempt the following exercise.

Assume that 0.100 mol of $CuSO_4:5H_2O$ is placed in each of the volumetric flasks shown (Fig. 7) and is properly diluted to the volumes shown. Calculate the concentration of each solution.

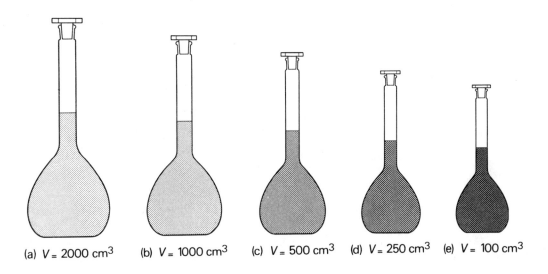

(a) $V = 2000$ cm³   (b) $V = 1000$ cm³   (c) $V = 500$ cm³   (d) $V = 250$ cm³   (e) $V = 100$ cm³

Fig. 7.

(Answers on page 62)

Calculating concentration from mass of solute and volume

Now we take this calculation a step further - be prepared for problems which give the mass of a substance, not the amount. These need an extra step at the start, i.e. dividing mass by molar mass to get amount using

$$n = \frac{m}{M}$$

Now attempt the following exercise.

Exercise 29   The table below indicates the masses of various compounds that were used to prepare the solutions of the stated volumes. Calculate the concentration of these solutions.

Compound	Mass/g	Volume/cm³
(a) $AgNO_3$	8.50	1000
(b) KIO_3	10.7	250
(c) $Pb(NO_3)_2$	11.2	50.0
(d) $K_2Cr_2O_7$	14.3	250
(e) $CuSO_4 \cdot 5H_2O$	11.9	500

(Answers on page 62)

You can now apply your knowledge of calculating concentrations to the preparation of a standard solution. Standard solutions are widely used in industrial research and teaching laboratories; it is important, therefore, that you should know how to prepare one.

Objectives.   After you have completed this experiment you should be able to:

(17) state the essential properties of a primary standard;

(18) prepare a standard solution.

If possible, watch the ILPAC videotape 'Preparing a Standard Solution' which shows the techniques involved. If the videotape is not available, ask your teacher whether you have enough laboratory experience simply to follow the experimental instructions.

You are about to watch a videotape. You are often required to record data during the programmes, so you should always have a pen and paper ready. Before you watch, find out whether you can see the programme more than once, and whether you can stop it at any point for discussion or note-taking.

If you have time, it is a good idea to watch the programme straight through first, and then make notes on the points you want to remember during a second showing. This method is particularly useful for a videotape such as this one, which shows you a specific technique.

EXPERIMENT 2
Preparing a standard solution

Aim

The purpose of this experiment is to prepare a standard solution of potassium hydrogenphthalate.

Introduction

Potassium hydrogenphthalate, $C_8H_5O_4K$, is a primary standard because it meets certain requirements.

1. It must be available in a highly pure state.

2. It must be stable in air.

3. It must be easily soluble in water.

4. It should have a high molar mass.

5. In solution, when used in volumetric analysis, it must undergo complete and rapid reaction.

You weigh accurately a sample of potassium hydrogenphthalate and use it to make a solution of concentration close to 0.10 mol dm^{-3}. In Experiment 3 you use this solution to determine the concentration of a solution of sodium hydroxide.

Requirements

safety spectacles
weighing bottle
spatula
potassium hydrogenphthalate, $C_8H_5O_4K$
access to a balance capable of weighing to within 0.01 g
beaker, 250 cm^3
wash bottle of distilled water
stirring rod with rubber end
volumetric flask, 250 cm^3, with label
filter funnel
dropping pipette

Procedure

1. Transfer between 4.8 and 5.4 g of potassium hydrogenphthalate into a weighing bottle and weigh it to the nearest 0.01 g.

2. Put about 50 cm^3 of water into a 250 cm^3 beaker. Carefully transfer the bulk of the potassium hydrogenphthalate from the weighing bottle into the beaker.

3. Reweigh the bottle with any remaining potassium hydrogenphthalate to the nearest 0.01 g.

4. Stir to dissolve the solid, adding more water if necessary.

5. Transfer the solution to the volumetric flask through the filter funnel. Rinse the beaker well, making sure all liquid goes into the volumetric flask. (Some workers transfer the solid directly into the flask through a filter funnel, but you should only do this if you are sure the solid will dissolve easily and if your funnel has a wide enough stem to prevent blockage.)

6. Add distilled water until the level is within about 1 cm of the mark on the neck of the flask. Insert the stopper and shake to mix the contents.

7. Using the dropping pipette, add enough water to bring the bottom of the meniscus to the mark as in Fig. 8. Insert the stopper and shake thoroughly ten times to ensure complete mixing. Simply inverting the flask once or twice does not mix the contents properly and is a very common fault.

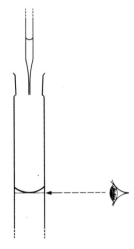

Fig. 8.

33

8. Label the flask with the contents, your name and the date. Leave a space for the concentration to be filled in after you have calculated it. Set aside the flask for Experiment 3 (in Level Two).

Results and Calculations

Using your data, you can fill in a copy of Results Table 6.

Results Table 6

Molar mass of potassium hydrogenphthalate, M	g mol^{-1}
Mass of bottle and contents before transfer, m_1	g
Mass of bottle and contents after transfer, m_2	g
Mass of potassium hydrogenphthalate, $m = (m_1 - m_2)$	g
Amount of potassium hydrogenphthalate, $n = m/M$	mol
Volume of solution, V	dm^{-3}
Concentration of potassium hydrogenphthalate, $c = n/V$	mol dm^{-3}

(Specimen results on page 63)

Questions

1. What effect would each of the errors described below have on the concentration of potassium hydrogenphthalate?

   (a) Some of the solid potassium hydrogenphthalate was spilled in making the transfer.

   (b) Not enough water was added to bring the volume up to the mark.

(Answers on page 63)

We now look at another type of calculation, but it is based on the same expression as are some of the problems you have already done.

Calculating the amount of substance in a solution

Often you want to know the amount of substance contained in a given volume of solution of known concentration.

To do this you substitute values for c and V into the expression:

$$c = \frac{n}{V} \quad \text{in the form} \quad n = cV$$

You use this in the next exercise.

Exercise 30   Calculate the amount of solute in each of the
               following solutions:

(a) 4.00 dm³ of 5.00 M NaOH,

(b) 1.00 dm³ of 2.50 M HCl,

(c) 20.0 cm³ of 0.439 M HNO₃.

(Answers on page **63**)

Now we take this calculation a step further, calculating the mass of solute
contained in a given volume of solution of known concentration. This needs
an extra step at the finish, i.e. multiplying amount by molar mass to get
mass $m = nM$.

Now try the next exercise.

Exercise 31   Calculate the mass of solute in the following
               solutions:

(a) 1.00 dm³ of 0.100 M NaCl,

(b) 500 cm³ of 1.00 M CaCl₂,

(c) 250 cm³ of 0.200 M KMnO₄,

(d) 200 cm³ of 0.117 M NaOH.

(Answers on page **63**)

*At the end of each Level, we collect together the objectives you have used in
that Level. For convenience, we have condensed some of the objectives but we
list them in the order in which they appeared so that you can easily check
your notes. You may find it helpful to write a very brief summary of the
contents using the objectives.*

LEVEL ONE CHECKLIST

You have now reached the end of Level One of this Unit. The following is a
list of the objectives in Level One. Read carefully through them and check
that you have adequate notes.

At this stage you should be able to:

(1)   calculate the masses of coins (or other items) relative to a chosen
       standard;

(2)   express masses in a variety of units;

(3)   define relative atomic mass in terms of carbon-12;

(4)   calculate the amount of identical objects given the mass of each object
       and the mass of unit amount of objects;

(5)   define (a) the mole, (b) molar mass;

(6)   quote the value of the Avogadro Constant to three significant figures;

(7)   calculate the molar mass of a substance, given its formula and a table of relative atomic masses;

(8)   calculate the amount of a substance, given its mass and molar mass;

(9)   calculate the number of particles in a given amount;

(10)   calculate the Avogadro Constant from data obtained in the monomolecular layer experiment;

(11)   do simple stoichiometric calculations;

(12)   calculate the empirical formula of a compound from composition data;

(13)   define concentration;

(14)   explain the term 'standard solution';

(15) & (16)   do calculations using the expression $c = \dfrac{n}{V}$;

(17)   state the essential properties of a primary standard.

(18)   prepare a standard solution.

LEVEL ONE TEST

After your revision based on the checklist, attempt the test which follows. The test is designed to show YOU what you should have learned. Where appropriate, A-level questions are included. Resist the temptation to study the questions beforehand.

If your teacher agrees, you could do the test at home. But remember to observe the rules — only you will lose if you cheat.

To find out how well you have learned the material in Level One, try the test which follows. Read the notes below before starting.

1. You should spend about 40 minutes on this test.

2. You will need a data book.

3. Hand your answers to your teacher for marking.

LEVEL ONE TEST

1. What mass of material is there in each of the following?

    (a) 2.00 mol of SO_3.

    (b) 0.0300 mol of Cl.

    (c) 9.00 mol of $SO_4{}^{2-}$.

    (d) 0.150 mol of $MgSO_4 \cdot 7H_2O$. (4)

2. What amount of each substance is contained in the following?

    (a) 31.0 g of P_4.

    (b) 1.00×10^{22} atoms of Cu.

    (c) 70.0 g of Fe^{2+}.

    (d) 9.00×10^{24} molecules of C_2H_5OH. (4)

3. The mass of one molecule of a compound is 2.19×10^{-22} g. What is the molar mass of the compound? (2)

4. What mass of aluminium, Al, is required to produce 1000 g of iron Fe according to the equation:

    $$3Fe_3O_4(s) + 8Al(s) \rightarrow 4Al_2O_3(s) + 9Fe(s) \qquad ?$$ (3)

5. A solution is made containing 2.38 g of magnesium chloride, $MgCl_2$, in 500 cm^3 of solution.

    (a) What is the concentration of magnesium chloride, $MgCl_2$, in this solution?

    (b) What is the concentration of chloride ions in this solution? (3)

6. A solution is made by dissolving 8.50 g of sodium nitrate, $NaNO_3$, and 16.40 g of calcium nitrate, $Ca(NO_3)_2$, in enough water to give 2000 cm^3 of solution.

    (a) What is the concentration of sodium ions in the solution?

    (b) What is the concentration of nitrate ions in the solution? (4)

7. A hydrated aluminium sulphate $Al_2(SO_4)_3 \cdot xH_2O$, contains 8.10% of aluminium by mass. Find the value of x. (5)

(Total: 25 marks)

LEVEL TWO

We now extend the concept of stoichiometry to reactions in solution, which you study by volumetric (titrimetric) analysis.

VOLUMETRIC ANALYSIS (TITRIMETRY)

A titration is a laboratory procedure where a measured volume of one solution is added to a known volume of another reagent until the reaction is complete. This operation is an example of volumetric (titrimetric) analysis. The stoichiometric point (equivalence point) is usually shown by the colour change of an indicator, and is then known as the end-point.

Volumetric analysis is a powerful technique which is used in a variety of ways by chemists in many different fields.

You perform three types of titration in this Unit:

(a)   an acid-base titration,

(b)   a redox titration,

(c)   a precipitation titration.

You may wish to leave some or all of the experiments in this section until you have started on the next Unit, Atomic Structure, which has few practicals. Ask your teacher about this.

Objectives.   When you have finished this section you should be able to:

(19)   calculate the concentration of a solution from titration data and the balanced equation;

(20)   perform titrations.

Calculating the concentration of a solution from titration data

Before you do a titration, we give a worked example to illustrate titrimetric calculations. For the worked example, we use an acid-base titration, but the method is applicable to all titrations.

Worked Example   20.0 cm^3 of a solution of barium hydroxide,
                      Ba(OH)$_2$, of unknown concentration is placed
                      in a conical flask and titrated with a solution
                      of hydrochloric acid, HCl, which has a concen-
                      tration of 0.0600 mol dm^{-3}. The volume of acid
                      required is 25.0 cm^3. Calculate the concentration
                      of the barium hydroxide solution.

$$Ba(OH)_2(aq) + 2HCl(aq) \rightarrow BaCl_2(aq) + 2H_2O(l)$$

<u>Solution</u>

This is a multi-step calculation. You may find it helpful to look again at the advice we gave on such calculations on page **24**. A summarised 'flow-chart' for the solution to this problem is:

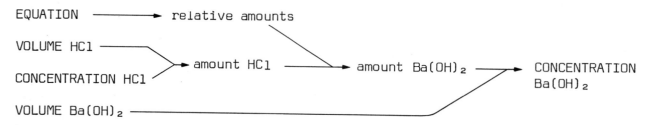

Now we look at the calculations, step by step.

1. Calculate the amount of HCl delivered (the solution of known concentration) by substitution into the expression

$$c = \frac{n}{V} \quad \text{in the form} \quad n = cV$$

   where c = 0.0600 mol dm^{-3} and V = (25.0/1000)dm^3 = 0.0250 dm^3

   $\therefore n = cV$ = 0.0600 mol dm^{-3} × 0.0250 dm^3 = 1.50 × 10^{-3} mol

2. Calculate the amount of Ba(OH)$_2$ (the solution of unknown concentration) which reacts with this amount of HCl by substituting into the expression derived from the equation:

$$\frac{\text{amount of Ba(OH)}_2}{\text{amount of HCl}} = \tfrac{1}{2}$$

$$\therefore \text{amount of Ba(OH)}_2 = \tfrac{1}{2} \text{ amount of HCl*}$$
$$= \tfrac{1}{2}(1.50 \times 10^{-3} \text{ mol})$$
$$= 7.50 \times 10^{-4} \text{ mol}$$

   *Always check this step carefully - it is easy to put the '$\tfrac{1}{2}$' in the wrong place.

3. Calculate the concentration of Ba(OH)$_2$ by substitution into the expression

$$c = \frac{n}{V}$$

   where n = 7.50 × 10^{-4} mol and V = 0.0200 dm^3

$$\therefore c = \frac{n}{V} = \frac{7.50 \times 10^{-4} \text{ mol}}{0.0200 \text{ dm}^3} = \boxed{0.0375 \text{ mol dm}^{-3}}$$

It is possible to derive a general expression to solve this problem and many like it. Remember, however, you should not use an expression unless you understand its derivation.

A general expression

Consider the general equation:

$$a\ A + b\ B \rightarrow \text{Products}$$

We can derive an expression relating concentration of A (c_A), concentration of B (c_B), volume of A (V_A), volume of B (V_B) and the stoichiometric coefficients a and b.

We start with a relation obtained directly from the chemical equation. It is:

$$\frac{\text{amount of A}}{\text{amount of B}} = \frac{a}{b}$$

We know that :

$$\text{amount of A} = c_A V_A$$

$$\text{amount of B} = c_B V_B$$

So, substituting for amount of A and amount of B in the first expression gives:

$$\boxed{\frac{c_A V_A}{c_B V_B} = \frac{a}{b}}$$

To help you use this expression correctly, remember that both A and a are on the top and both B and b are on the bottom.

This expression is very useful for solving titrimetric problems and we use it in our answers to such problems wherever appropriate. However, it may not always provide the best way to tackle a particular problem.

Now we give you some practice in doing volumetric calculations.

Exercise 32   (a)   Solve the Worked Example on page **39** using the expression we derived.

(b)   Why is it not necessary to convert volumes in cm^3 to dm^3 when using the expression?

(Answers on page **63**)

Exercise 33   What volume of sodium hydroxide solution, 0.500 M NaOH, is needed to neutralise

(a) 50.0 cm^3 of nitric acid, 0.100 M HNO_3,

$$NaOH(aq) + HNO_3(aq) \rightarrow NaNO_3(aq) + H_2O(l)$$

(b) 22.5 cm^3 of sulphuric acid, 0.262 M H_2SO_4,

$$2NaOH(aq) + H_2SO_4(aq) \rightarrow Na_2SO_4(aq) + 2H_2O(l)$$

(Answers on page **64**) '

Although you most often start your calculations knowing the equation for the reaction, you may sometimes have to derive the equation, as in the next exercise.

Exercise 34 As a result of a titration, it was found that
25.0 cm³ of silver nitrate solution, 0.50 M AgNO₃,
reacted with 31.3 cm³ of barium chloride solution,
0.20 M BaCl₂. Use these results to determine the
stoichiometric coefficients, a and b, in the
equation:

$$a \text{ AgNO}_3(aq) + b \text{ BaCl}_2 \rightarrow \text{ Products}$$

(Answer on page **64**)

Now that you know how to use titration results in calculations
you can perform a titration for yourself. The experimental
techniques are worth studying before you begin.

The ILPAC videotape 'Performing a Titration' shows you the
standard techniques of performing a titration. If possible
you should watch this before you do the next experiment.

If the tape is not available, read about these techniques in a
suitable book suggested by your teacher, or ask for a demonstration.

EXPERIMENT 3
An acid-base titration

Aim

The purpose of this experiment is to determine the
concentration of a solution of sodium hydroxide by
titration against a standard solution of potassium
hydrogenphthalate.

Introduction

You have already made a standard solution of potassium hydrogenphthalate,
a primary standard. The substance has the formula $C_8H_5O_4K$, but because it
behaves as a monoprotic (monobasic) acid in producing one mole of hydrogen
ions per mole of compound, we can simplify the formula to HA. This simple
formula is often used to represent an acid with a complicated structure.

Sodium hydroxide reacts with potassium hydrogenphthalate according to the equation:

$$\text{C}_6\text{H}_4(\text{CO}_2\text{H})(\text{CO}_2^-\text{K}^+)\text{(aq)} + \text{Na}^+\text{OH}^-\text{(aq)} \rightarrow \text{C}_6\text{H}_4(\text{CO}_2^-\text{Na}^+)(\text{CO}_2^-\text{K}^+)\text{(aq)} + \text{H}_2\text{O}$$

or $\text{HA(aq)} + \text{Na}^+\text{OH}^-\text{(aq)} \rightarrow \text{Na}^+\text{A}^-\text{(aq)} + \text{H}_2\text{O(l)}$

To show you when the reaction is complete - the stoichiometric point or equivalent point - you use an indicator called phenolphthalein, which is colourless in acid and pink in alkaline solution. The point at which the addition of one drop (or even less) of alkali changes the solution from colourless to just faintly pink is called the end-point and, in this case, shows that the reaction is just complete.

Requirements

safety spectacles
filter funnel, small
burette, 50 cm^3, and stand
2 beakers, 100 cm^3
sodium hydroxide solution, approx. 0.1 M NaOH – – – – – – – – – – – – – –
pipette, 25 cm^3
pipette filler
standard potassium hydrogenphthalate solution (prepared in Experiment 2)
4 conical flasks, 250 cm^3
phenolphthalein indicator solution
white tile
wash bottle of distilled water

Procedure

1. Using the funnel, rinse the burette with the sodium hydroxide solution and fill it with the same solution. Do not forget to rinse and fill the tip. Record the initial burette reading in the 'Trial' column of Results Table 7.

2. Using a pipette filler, rinse the pipette with some of the potassium hydrogenphthalate solution and carefully transfer 25.0 cm^3 of the solution to a clean 250 cm^3 conical flask.

3. Add 2-3 drops of the phenolphthalein indicator solution.

4. Run sodium hydroxide solution from the burette into the flask, with swirling, until the solution just turns pink. This first flask may be used as a trial run, because you will probably overshoot the end-point. Record the final burette reading.

5. Refill the burette with the sodium hydroxide solution, and again record the initial burette reading to the nearest 0.05 cm^3 (one drop).

6. Using the pipette, transfer 25.0 cm^3 of the potassium hydrogenphthalate solution to another clean conical flask. Add 2-3 drops of the phenol-phthalein indicator solution.

7. Carefully titrate this solution to the end-point, adding the alkali drop by drop when you think the colour is about to change.

8. Repeat steps 5, and 7 at least twice more.

9. Empty the burette and wash it carefully immediately after the titration, especially if it has a ground glass tap.

Accuracy

You should record burette readings to the nearest 0.05 cm³ (approximately one drop). Consecutive titrations should agree to within 0.10 cm³ and, strictly, you should repeat the titration until this is achieved. However, you may have neither the time nor the materials to do this. With practice, your technique will improve so that it is not necessary to do more than four titrations. Calculate the mean of the two (or preferably three) closest consecutive readings and quote this also to the nearest 0.05 cm³. Note that this does not introduce a fourth significant figure; it merely makes the third figure more reliable.

Results Table 7

Pipette solution				mol dm⁻³		cm³
Burette solution				mol dm⁻³		
Indicator						
		Trial	1	2	3	(4)
Burette readings	Final					
	Initial					
Volume used (titre)/cm³						
Mean titre/cm³						

Calculation

1. Calculate the concentration of the sodium hydroxide solution.

(Specimen results on page 64)

Questions

1. What effect would each of the errors described below have on the calculated value of the concentration of sodium hydroxide?

    (a) The burette is not rinsed with the sodium hydroxide solution.

    (b) The pipette is not rinsed with the potassium hydrogenphthalate solution.

    (c) The tip of the burette is not filled before titration begins.

    (d) The conical flask contains some distilled water before the addition of potassium hydrogenphthalate.

2. In using phenolphthalein as an indicator, we prefer to titrate from a colourless to pink solution rather than from pink to colourless. Suggest a reason for this.

3. Why is it advisable to remove sodium hydroxide from the burette as soon as possible after the titration?

(Answers on page 64)

In the next experiment, you perform another titration but this
time you titrate a solution of an oxidant into a solution of a
reductant. This type of titration is called a redox titration.

Objective. After you complete this experiment you should be able to:

(21) use titration data to determine the stoichiometry of a reaction.

EXPERIMENT 4
A redox titration

Aim

The purpose of this experiment is to balance the
equation for the reaction between sodium
thiosulphate and iodine.

$$a \text{ Na}_2\text{S}_2\text{O}_3(\text{aq}) + b \text{ I}_2(\text{aq}) \rightarrow \text{ Products}$$

Introduction

You are to determine the ratio of a to b and so determine the stoichiometry
of the reaction. You do this by taking a known amount of iodine and titra-
ting it with standard sodium thiosulphate.

The indicator you use in this titration is starch solution, which is deep blue
in the presence of iodine; it is added near the end of the titration when the
solution is straw-coloured. If you add starch too soon, you may get a blue-
black precipitate which does not dissolve again easily even though there is an
excess of thiosulphate. The end-point in this titration is the point at which
the addition of one drop of sodium thiosulphate causes the disappearance of
the deep-blue colour.

Requirements

safety spectacles
filter funnel
burette, 50 cm^3, and stand
2 beakers, 100 cm^3
sodium thiosulphate solution, standardised
pipette, 10 cm^3
pipette filler
iodine solution, standardised
4 conical flasks, 250 cm^3
starch indicator solution
white tile
wash bottle of distilled water

Procedure

1. Using the funnel, rinse the burette and tip with the sodium thiosulphate solution. Fill it with the same solution. Don't forget to fill the tip. Record the initial burette reading in Results Table 8.

2. Rinse the pipette with some of the iodine solution and carefully transfer 10.0 cm³ of the solution to one of the conical flasks.

3. Titrate this solution until the colour of the iodine has <u>almost</u> gone (as indicated by a pale straw colour).

4. Add 1-2 cm³ of starch solution and continue the titration, adding sodium thiosulphate dropwise until the end-point. Use the first flask for a trial run. Record the final burette reading.

5. Repeat the titration three more times. Enter your results into a copy of Results Table 8. These titrations should agree to within 0.10 cm³.

Results Table 8

Pipette solution				mol dm⁻³		cm³
Burette solution				mol dm⁻³		
Indicator						
		Trial	1	2	3	(4)
Burette readings	Final					
	Initial					
Volume used (titre)/cm³						
Mean titre/cm³						

Calculation

1. Use your results to determine the stoichiometric coefficients, a and b, in the equation:

$$a \ Na_2S_2O_3(aq) + b \ I_2(aq) \rightarrow Products$$

2. All the iodine forms sodium iodide NaI. There is one other product - work out its formula.

(Specimen results on page **65**)

In the next experiment you perform another titration, where you titrate a solution of silver nitrate into a solution of a halide. This type of titration is called a precipitation titration.

After you complete this experiment you should be able to:

(22) determine the number of molecules of water of hydration from titration
      data.

In this experiment, you make a standard solution of barium chloride.
If you do not remember the technique, watch the ILPAC videotape
'Preparing a Standard Solution' or re-read the instructions given
in Experiment 2. The ILPAC videotape 'Performing a Titration' also
shows you the colour change to look for at the end-point.

EXPERIMENT 5
A precipitation titration

Aim

The purpose of this experiment is to determine
the number of molecules of water of hydration
in hydrated barium chloride, i.e. to calculate
the value of x in the formula $BaCl_2 \cdot xH_2O$

Introduction

You titrate chloride ion with silver ion, according to the equation:

$$Ag^+(aq) + Cl^-(aq) \rightarrow AgCl(s)$$

This provides you with the data necessary to do the calculations. The indicator for the titration is potassium chromate(VI). When all the chloride
ions have reacted, any more silver ions react with the indicator producing a
red precipitate of silver chromate(VI). This is because silver chloride is
less soluble than silver chromate(VI).

$$2Ag^+(aq) + CrO_4{}^{2-}(aq) \rightarrow Ag_2CrO_4(s)$$

The end-point in this reaction is when one drop of silver ion produces a red
tinge on the precipitate of silver chloride.

Barium ions also react with chromate ions so the barium must be removed by
adding sulphate ions:

$$Ba^{2+}(aq) + SO_4{}^{2-}(aq) \rightarrow BaSO_4(s)$$

This does not affect the concentration of chloride ions.

Requirements

safety spectacles
weighing bottle
spatula
barium chloride crystals ———————————————————————
access to balance capable of weighing to 0.01 g
beaker, 250 cm^3
wash bottle of distilled water
stirring rod with rubber end
volumetric flask, 250 cm^3, with label
filter funnel
dropping pipette
burette, 50 cm^3, and stand
2 beakers, 100 cm^3
silver nitrate solution, standardised ———————————
pipette, 10 cm^3
pipette filler
4 conical flasks, 250 cm^3
sodium sulphate
potassium chromate solution
'silver residues' bottle

Hazard Warning

Barium chloride is very poisonous.
Silver nitrate is also poisonous and
can stain the skin.
Therefore you MUST:

USE THE PIPETTE FILLER SUPPLIED

WASH YOUR HANDS AFTER USE

Procedure

1. Prepare a standard solution of hydrated barium chloride by accurately weighing out between 1.4 g and 1.6 g of the salt. Dissolve this and make up to 250 cm^3 in a volumetric flask. Fill in a copy of Results Table 9.

2. Rinse the burette with some silver nitrate solution and fill. Don't forget the tip.

3. Rinse the 10.0 cm^3 pipette with barium chloride solution, and transfer 10.0 cm^3 to a conical flask.

4. Add about 1 g of sodium sulphate crystals to the flask and swirl it.

5. Add 2-3 drops of potassium chromate(VI) indicator. Titrate the solution to the end-point, as shown by the first appearance of a permanent but faint reddish precipitate of silver chromate(VI). Use the first flask for a trial run. Enter your results in a copy of Results Table 10.

6. Repeat steps 2 to 5 three times. Don't wash the contents of the titration flasks down the sink - pour them into a 'silver residue' bottle.

Results and calculations

Results Table 9

Mass of bottle and contents before transfer, m_1		g
Mass of bottle and contents after transfer, m_2		g
Mass of sample, $m = (m_1 - m_2)$		g
Mass of $BaCl_2 : H_2O$ in 10.0 cm^3		g

Results Table 10

Pipette solution						mol dm^{-3}	cm^3
Burette solution						mol dm^{-3}	
Indicator							
		Trial	1	2	3	(4)	
Burette readings	Final						
	Initial						
Volume used (titre)/cm^3							
Mean titre/cm^3							

Calculation

1. From the mean titre and concentration of silver nitrate, calculate the amount of chloride ion present in a 10.0 cm^3 sample.

2. Calculate the mass of anhydrous barium chloride, $BaCl_2$, present in a sample.

3. Calculate the mass of water present by subtracting the mass of $BaCl_2$ from the mass of $BaCl_2 \cdot x H_2O$.

4. Determine the ratio of amount of $BaCl_2$ to amount of H_2O and thus the value of x.

(Specimen results on page 65 and 66)

A flow-chart for this multi-step calculation is as follows:

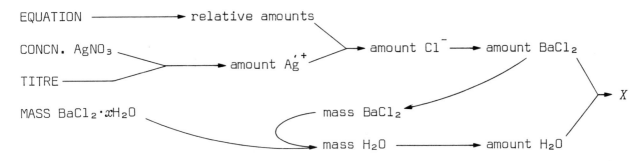

The calculation in the last experiment should help you to do the next exercise, which is part of an A-level question. We suggest that if you find it difficult, you look at our introduction to the Worked Example on page 24 and sketch out a flow-chart before you begin.

Exercise 35   When 0.203 g of hydrated magnesium chloride, $MgCl_m \cdot nH_2O$, was dissolved in water and titrated with 0.100 M silver nitrate ($AgNO_3$) solution, 20.0 cm^3 of the latter were required. A sample of the hydrated chloride lost 53.2% of its mass when heated in a stream of hydrogen chloride, leaving a residue of anhydrous magnesium chloride. From these figures, calculate the values of m and n.

(Answers on page 66)

LEVEL TWO CHECKLIST

You have now reached the end of this Unit. Look again at the checklist at the end of Level One. In addition, you should now be able to:

(19)   calculate the concentration of a solution from titration data and the balanced equation for the reaction;

(20)   perform titrations;

(21)   use titration data to determine the stoichiometry of a reaction;

(22)   determine the number of molecules of water of hydration from titration data.

Check that you have adequate notes before going on to the End-of-Unit Test.

It is a good idea to summarise the contents of each Unit on a single sheet of paper. Look at the section on note-taking in the Students' Introduction to ILPAC - you may find it helpful to make a 'patterned' summary.

END-OF-UNIT TEST

To test both your practical skill and your ability to calculate, we base the end-of-Unit test on an experiment. (In all other Units, the tests are written, but a practical test is appropriate for this Unit.)

Let your teacher know when you are ready for the Test.

END-OF-UNIT TEST (a practical test)

Aim

The purpose of this experiment is to determine x in the formula $Fe(NH_4)_2(SO_4)_2 \cdot xH_2O$ by titration against a standard solution of potassium manganate(VII) (permanganate).

The directions are similar to those that would be given by an examination board.

   A is a solution of ammonium iron(II) sulphate, $Fe(NH_4)_2(SO_4)_2 \cdot xH_2O$, the precise concentration of which is given by the teacher.

   B is a solution of potassium manganate(VII) (permanganate), $KMnO_4$, the precise concentration of which is given by the teacher.

Procedure

Pipette 25 cm³ of the ammonium iron(II) sulphate solution, A, into a conical flask and add an equal volume of dilute sulphuric acid. Titrate with potassium manganate(VII) solution, B, until a permanent faint pink colour appears. Repeat the titration twice and enter your results in a copy of Results Table 11.

The overall equation for the reaction is

$$MnO_4^-(aq) + 5Fe^{2+}(aq) + 8H^+(aq) \rightarrow Mn^{2+}(aq) + 5Fe^{3+}(aq) + 4H_2O(l)$$

Results Table 11

							mol dm^{-3}	cm³
Pipette solution								
Burette solution							mol dm^{-3}	
Indicator								
		Trial	1		2	3	(4)	
Burette readings	Final							
	Initial							
Volume used (titre)/cm³								
Mean titre/cm³								

Calculation

Use your results to determine x in the formula $Fe(NH_4)_2(SO_4)_2 \cdot xH_2O$. You should set out your calculations so that every step in your working is clearly shown. If you cannot work out a method of calculation, use the suggestions on the next page.

Hand your results table and calculations to your teacher for marking.

Calculation steps

1. From the titre and the equation for the reaction calculate the concentration of Fe^{2+} ion.

2. From the concentration calculate the mass of anhydrous $Fe(NH_4)_2(SO_4)_2$ in one litre of solution.

3. Subtract the mass obtained in step 2 from the mass of the salt in one litre. This difference equals $18x$ g.

APPENDIX

SIGNIFICANT FIGURES & SCIENTIFIC MEASUREMENTS

These notes on the use of significant figures are not rigorous. We merely give some useful rules which you can apply to ordinary A-level calculations. For a detailed treatment you can read a text-book on the theory of measurements.

The numerical value of any physical measurement is an approximation which is limited by the accuracy of the measuring instrument.

Generally, the last digit in a measured quantity has an uncertainty associated with it. For example, in reading a thermometer, part of which is shown in Fig. 9, some may read the temperature as 21.1°C and some may read it as 21.2°C or 21.3°C.

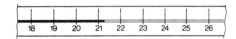

Fig. 9.

That is, there is no doubt that the temperature is between twenty-one and twenty-two degrees centigrade, but there is some uncertainty in the last place. It is for this reason that we must consider the use of significant figures. Furthermore, it is important to consider the use of significant figures when so many calculations are made using electronic calculators which give as many as ten digits on their displays. You are very rarely justified in using all of them.

Zeros

A measured mass of 23 g has two significant figures, 2 and 3. If this same mass were written as 0.023 kg, it still contains two significant figures because zeros appearing as the first figures of a number are not significant - they merely locate the decimal point. However, the mass 0.0230 kg is expressed to three significant figures (2, 3 and the last 0).

The expression 'the length is 4700 m' does not necessarily show the accuracy of the measurement. To do this, the number should be written in standard form. If the measurement is made only to the nearest 1000 m, we use only one significant figure, i.e. $\ell = 5 \times 10^3$ m.

A more precise measurement, to the nearest 100 m, merits two significant figures, i.e. $\ell = 4.7 \times 10^3$ m, and so on as summarised in Table 3.

Table 3

Distance ℓ/m	Significant figures	Range of uncertainty	Precision of measurement
4700	unspecified	unspecified	unspecified
5×10^3	1	4.5 to 5.5	nearest 1000 m
4.7×10^3	2	4.65 to 4.75	nearest 100 m
4.70×10^3	3	4.695 to 4.705	nearest 10 m
4.700×10^3	4	4.6995 to 4.7005	nearest 1 m

Here is an exercise to see if you can recognise the number of significant figures in a measured quantity.

Exercise 36   How many significant figures are in the following quantities?

(a) 2.54 g   (d) 14.0 cm^3 (g) 9.993 g cm^{-3}

(b) 2.205 g   (e) 1.86 x 10^5 s   (h) 5070 m s^{-1}

(c) 1.1 g   (f) 2.0070 g   (i) 127 000 kg

(Answers on page 65)

Now we look at significant figures in the results of combining uncertain values in calculations.

Addition and subtraction

After addition or subtraction, the answer should be rounded off to keep only the same number of decimal places as the least precise item. Here are some Worked Examples.

Worked Examples   Add the following quantities:

(a) 46.247 cm^3

3.219 cm^3

0.224 cm^3

49.690 cm^3 Answer: 49.690 cm^3

Each volume to be added is expressed to the nearest 0.001 cm^3, so we can express the answer also to the nearest 0.001 cm^3.

(b) 26.6   cm^3

0.0028   cm^3

0.00002 cm^3

26.60282 cm^3 Answer: 26.6 cm^3

The number 26.6 is expressed to one place past the decimal point so you cannot have the answer quoted to a greater accuracy than one place past the decimal point.

(c) 2.40   cm^3

3.6584 cm^3

0.029   cm^3

6.0874 cm^3 Answer: 6.09 cm^3

The reasoning here is the same as in part (b). The least accurate measurement is 2.40 cm^3 so, in the answer, the volume cannot be quoted to more than two places past the decimal point. In this case, however, we round up rather than round down.

The reasoning is the same for subtraction.

Worked Examples   Perform the following subtractions :

            (a) 7.26 g

               - 0.2 g
               ─────────
                 7.06 g   Answer: 7.1 g

            (b) 539.27 g

               - 12.8 g
               ─────────
                 526.47 g   Answer: 526.5 g

Try the following exercises:

Exercise 37   Add the following, expressing your answer to the
                  correct number of significant figures:

            (a) 203   g

                  4   g

                0.77 g
               ────────

            (b) 0.0034 dm³

                0.094 dm³

                0.552 dm³
               ────────

            (Answers on page 65)

Exercise 38   Perform the following subtractions :

            (a) 4.0   m

               - 0.623 m
               ────────

            (b)   76   cm³

               - 0.3 cm³
               ────────

            (Answers on page 65)

The rules for multiplication and division are even easier.

Multiplication and division

The result of multiplying or dividing can contain only as many significant figures as are contained in the factor with the least number of significant figures.

Worked Example   Calculate the density of an object which weighs 17.32 g and has a volume of 2.4 cm^3.

Solution

$$\text{density} \ = \ \frac{\text{mass}}{\text{volume}} \ = \ \frac{17.32 \text{ g}}{2.4 \text{ cm}^3}$$

A calculator gives the result as 7.2166667 g cm^{-3}. But the volume has the fewer number of significant figures - two. So the result is rounded off to 7.2 g cm^{-3}.

Now do the next exercise.

Exercise 39   Multiply the following, expressing your answer to the correct number of significant figures:

(a) 0.11 mol dm^{-3} × 0.0272 dm^3

(b) 2.43 mol × 27.9 g mol^{-1}

(Answers on page 65)

Exercise 40   Divide the following, expressing your answer to the correct number of significant figures:

(a) $\dfrac{9.2 \text{ g}}{19.00 \text{ g mol}^{-1}}$

(b) $\dfrac{0.20 \text{ g}}{0.1 \text{ cm}^3}$

(Answers on page 65)

ANSWERS

Exercise 1   Specimen results

Results Table 1

Coin	Number of coins	Total mass/g	Average mass/g
½p	37	65.79	1.778
1p	12	43.12	3.593
2p	9	63.49	7.054
5p	8	45.16	5.645
10p	10	110.68	11.068

Exercise 2, 3 and 4   Specimen results

Results Table 2

Coin	1 Average mass/g	Relative masses using different standards			
		2 mass/HCU	3 mass/OCU	4 mass/CCU	
½p	1.778	1.000	0.990	0.998	
1p	3.593	2.021	2.000	2.016	
2p	7.054	3.967	3.927	3.958	
5p	5.645	3.175	3.142	3.168	
10p	11.068	6.225	6.161	6.211	

Exercise 5

Results Table 3

Element	Relative Atomic Mass (R.A.M.)			
	H scale	O scale	12C scale	
H	1.00000	1.00794	1.00790	
He	3.97123	4.00276	4.00260	
Li	6.88459	6.93924	6.93897	
C	11.9169	12.0115	12.0111	
O	15.8740	16.0000	15.9994	
Na	22.8096	22.9907	22.9898	
Ar	39.6349	39.9496	39.9480	
U	236.164	238.039	238.030	

Exercise 6   Specimen results

Results Table 4

Coin	1 Total mass of coins in jar/g	2 Mass per dozen /g doz^{-1}	3 Amount in jar/doz
½p	32.04	21.34	1.50
1p	64.63	43.12	1.50
2p	126.90	84.65	1.50

Exercise 7

$$\text{amount} = \frac{\text{mass}}{\text{mass per dozen}} = \frac{5265 \text{ g}}{45.0 \text{ g doz}^{-1}} = \boxed{125 \text{ doz}}$$

Exercise 8

(a)
$$\text{amount} = \frac{\text{mass}}{\text{mass per gross}} = \frac{5.13 \times 10^6 \text{ g}}{82.08 \text{ g gross}^{-1}} = \boxed{6.25 \times 10^4 \text{ gross}}$$

(b)
$$\text{number} = \text{amount} \times \text{number per amount} = 6.25 \times 10^4 \text{ gross} \times 144 \text{ gross}^{-1}$$
$$= \boxed{9.00 \times 10^6}$$

Exercise 9

(a)
$$\text{time} = \frac{\text{number of molecules}}{\text{rate of removal}} = \frac{1.67 \times 10^{23}}{1 \text{ s}^{-1}}$$
$$= \boxed{1.67 \times 10^{23} \text{ s}}$$

(b)
$$1 \text{ y} = 365 \text{ dy} \times \frac{24 \text{ hr}}{\text{dy}} \times \frac{60 \text{ min}}{\text{hr}} \times \frac{60 \text{ s}}{\text{min}} = 3.15 \times 10^7 \text{ s}$$
$$\therefore 1 \text{ s} = \frac{1 \text{ y}}{3.15 \times 10^7}$$
$$\therefore \text{ time taken} = 1.67 \times 10^{23} \text{ s} = 1.67 \times 10^{23} \times \frac{1 \text{ y}}{3.15 \times 10^7} = \boxed{5.30 \times 10^{15} \text{ y}}$$

Exercise 10

(a) $\boxed{17.0 \text{ g mol}^{-1}}$ $14.0 + 3(1.0) = 17.0$

(b) $\boxed{199.9 \text{ g mol}^{-1}}$ $40.1 + 2(79.9) = 199.9$

(c) $\boxed{98.0 \text{ g mol}^{-1}}$ $3(1.0) + 31.0 + 4(16.0) = 98.0$

(d) $\boxed{322.1 \text{ g mol}^{-1}}$ $2(23.0) + 32.1 + 4(16.0) + 20(1.0) + 10(16.0) = 322.1$

Exercise 11

(a) 35.5 g

(b) 71.0 g

(c) 31.0 g

(d) 124.0 g

(e) 126.9 g (ignore the mass of the extra electrons)

Exercise 12

(a) Substituting into the expression

$$n = \frac{m}{M}$$

where m = 30.0 g and M = 32.0 g mol⁻¹

gives $n = \dfrac{m}{M} = \dfrac{30.0\ g}{32.0\ g\ mol^{-1}} = \boxed{0.938\ mol}$

(b) $n = \dfrac{m}{M} = \dfrac{31.0\ g}{124.0\ g\ mol^{-1}} = \boxed{0.250\ mol}$

(c) $n = \dfrac{m}{M} = \dfrac{50.0\ g}{100.0\ g\ mol^{-1}} = \boxed{0.500\ mol}$

Exercise 13

(a) Substituting into the expression

$$n = \frac{m}{M}$$ in the form $m = nM$

where n = 1.00 mol and M = 2.00 g mol⁻¹

gives $m = nM$ = 1.00 mol × 2.00 g mol⁻¹ = $\boxed{2.00\ g}$

(b) $m = nM$ = 0.500 mol × 58.5 g mol⁻¹ = $\boxed{29.3\ g}$

(c) $m = nM$ = 0.250 mol × 44.0 g mol⁻¹ = $\boxed{11.0\ g}$

Exercise 14

(a) Substituting into the expression

$$n = \frac{m}{M}$$

where m = 1.00 g, M = 17.0 g mol⁻¹

gives $n = \dfrac{m}{M} = \dfrac{1.00\ g}{17.0\ g\ mol^{-1}} = \boxed{0.0588\ mol}$

(b) If the number of molecules is to be the same, then the amount must be the same. For SO_2, M = 64.1 g mol⁻¹ and from (a), n = 0.0588 mol

∴ substituting these values in the expression

$$n = \frac{m}{M}$$ in the form $m = nM$

gives $m = nM$ = 0.0588 mol × 64.1 g mol⁻¹ = $\boxed{3.77\ g}$

Exercise 15

(a) Substituting into the expression

$$n = \frac{m}{M}$$

where m = 18.0 g, M = 12.0 g mol⁻¹

gives $n = \dfrac{m}{M} = \dfrac{18.0\ g}{12.0\ g\ mol^{-1}} = 1.50\ mol$

Substituting into the expression

$$N = nL$$

where n = 1.50 mol, L = 6.02 × 10²³ mol⁻¹

gives $N = nL$ = 1.50 mol × 6.02 × 10²³ mol⁻¹ = 9.03 × 10²³

Or, substituting $n = \dfrac{m}{M}$ into the expression $N = nL$

gives $N = \dfrac{mL}{M} = \dfrac{18.0\ g \times 6.02 \times 10^{23}\ mol^{-1}}{12.0\ g\ mol^{-1}} = \boxed{9.03 \times 10^{23}}$

(b) $N = \dfrac{mL}{M} = \dfrac{18.0\ g \times 6.02 \times 10^{23}\ mol^{-1}}{63.5\ g\ mol^{-1}} = \boxed{1.71 \times 10^{23}}$

(c) $N = \dfrac{mL}{M} = \dfrac{7.20\ g \times 6.02 \times 10^{23}\ mol^{-1}}{32.1\ g\ mol^{-1}} = \boxed{1.35 \times 10^{23}}$

Note that in (c), the number of atoms is the same whatever the molecular formula.

Exercise 16

(a) Substituting into the expression

$$n = \frac{m}{M}$$

where m = 1.00 g, M = 17.0 g mol⁻¹

gives $n = \dfrac{1.00\ g}{17.0\ g\ mol^{-1}} = 0.0588\ mol$

Substituting into the expression

$$N = nL$$

gives N = 0.0588 mol × 6.02 × 10²³ mol⁻¹ = $\boxed{3.54 \times 10^{22}}$

Or, combining $n = \dfrac{m}{M}$ with $N = nL$ and substituting gives

$N = \dfrac{mL}{M} = \dfrac{1.00\ g \times 6.02 \times 10^{23}\ mol^{-1}}{17.0\ g\ mol^{-1}} = \boxed{3.54 \times 10^{22}}$

(b) $N = \dfrac{mL}{M} = \dfrac{3.28\ g \times 6.02 \times 10^{23}\ mol^{-1}}{64.1\ g\ mol^{-1}} = \boxed{3.08 \times 10^{22}}$

(c) $N = \dfrac{mL}{M} = \dfrac{7.20\ g \times 6.02 \times 10^{23}\ mol^{-1}}{8 \times 32.1\ g\ mol^{-1}} = \boxed{1.69 \times 10^{22}}$

Results Table 5

Number of drops to deliver 1.0 cm³ of solution	Number of drops delivered to make monomolecular layer	Diameter of monomolecular layer/cm
100	12	11.2

1. Volume of 1 drop = $\dfrac{1.0 \text{ cm}^3}{100}$ = $\boxed{0.010 \text{ cm}^3}$

2. Since 1000 cm³ of solution contains 0.050 cm³ of oleic acid

   1.00 cm³ of solution contains $\dfrac{0.050 \text{ cm}^3}{1000}$ of oleic acid

   ∴ 0.010 cm³ of solution contains $\dfrac{0.050 \text{ cm}^3 \times 0.010}{1000}$ of oleic acid

   $= \boxed{5.0 \times 10^{-7} \text{ cm}^3}$

3. Volume of oleic acid in monomolecular layer = $5.0 \times 10^{-7} \text{ cm}^3 \times 12$

   $= \boxed{6.0 \times 10^{-6} \text{ cm}^3}$

4. $A = \dfrac{3.142 \times (11.2 \text{ cm})^2}{4}$ = $\boxed{98.5 \text{ cm}^2}$

5. Thickness $= \dfrac{\text{volume}}{\text{area}}$ $= \dfrac{6.0 \times 10^{-6} \text{ cm}^3}{98.5 \text{ cm}^2}$ = $\boxed{6.1 \times 10^{-8} \text{ cm}}$

6. Volume of one molecule $= (6.1 \times 10^{-8} \text{ cm})^3$ = $\boxed{2.3 \times 10^{-22} \text{ cm}^3}$

7. Density $= \dfrac{\text{molar mass}}{\text{molar volume}}$

   ∴ molar volume $= \dfrac{\text{molar mass}}{\text{density}}$ $= \dfrac{282 \text{ g mol}^{-1}}{0.890 \text{ g cm}^{-3}}$ = $\boxed{317 \text{ cm}^3 \text{ mol}^{-1}}$

8. $L = \dfrac{\text{molar volume}}{\text{volume of molecule}}$ $= \dfrac{317 \text{ cm}^3 \text{ mol}^{-1}}{2.3 \times 10^{-22} \text{ cm}^3}$ = $\boxed{1.4 \times 10^{24} \text{ mol}^{-1}}$

(The accepted value of $L = 6.02 \times 10^{23} \text{ mol}^{-1}$. You should expect to obtain a value of L to within one power of 10, i.e. between $6.0 \times 10^{22} \text{ mol}^{-1}$ and $5.0 \times 10^{24} \text{ mol}^{-1}$.)

Exercise 17

(a) 0.500 mol of NaCl contains 0.500 mol of Na^+ and 0.500 mol of Cl^-

∴ Total amount of ions, $n = 1.00$ mol

Substituting into the expression

$N = nL$

gives $N = 1.00 \text{ mol} \times 6.02 \times 10^{23} \text{ mol}^{-1}$ = $\boxed{6.02 \times 10^{23}}$

(b) The amount of NaCl is calculated by substituting into the expression

$n = \dfrac{m}{M}$

where $m = 14.6$ g and $M = 58.5$ g mol⁻¹

∴ $n = \dfrac{14.6 \text{ g}}{58.5 \text{ g mol}^{-1}}$ = 0.250 mol

0.250 mol of NaCl contains 0.250 mol of Na^+ and 0.250 of Cl^-

∴ total amount of ions, $n = 0.500$ mol

Substituting into the expression

$N = nL$

gives $N = 0.500 \text{ mol} \times 6.02 \times 10^{23} \text{ mol}^{-1}$ = $\boxed{3.01 \times 10^{23}}$

(c) The amount of CaCl₂ is given by substituting in the expression

$n = \dfrac{m}{M}$

where $m = 18.5$ g and $M = 111.0$ g mol⁻¹

∴ $n = \dfrac{18.5 \text{ g}}{111.0 \text{ g mol}^{-1}}$ = 0.167 mol

Since each mole of CaCl₂ contains 3 mol of ions (Ca^{2+}, Cl^-, Cl^-), the amount of ions, $n = 3 \times 0.167 \text{ mol} = 0.501$ mol

Substituting into the expression

$N = nL$

gives $N = 0.501 \text{ mol} \times 6.02 \times 10^{23} \text{ mol}^{-1}$ = $\boxed{3.01 \times 10^{23}}$

Experiment 1 - Questions

1. The various sources of error which may account for the difference between the experimental and actual value for L are as follows:

   (a) the number of drops required to make a monomolecular layer was inaccurately measured;

   (b) not all the pentane had evaporated from the surface;

   (c) the volume of the drop was inaccurately determined;

   (d) the molecules were unevenly dispersed on the surface of the film, i.e. there was more than one layer of molecules on parts of the film;

   (e) the assumption about the shape of the molecule was incorrect. In fact, the molecule is rather more the shape of a cylinder than a cube.

2. The number of drops required to fill the loop is subject to the greatest error. Even if you are sure to the nearest drop, this gives only two significant figures (or only one for a small loop!) whereas all the other values are obtained to three significant figures.

3. A substitute for pentane must:

   (a) dissolve oleic acid readily;

   (b) evaporate readily;

   (c) not react with oleic acid;

   (d) not react with water;

   (e) not dissolve in water.

Exercise 18

(a) From the equation for the reaction we know that

amount of Mg = amount of S

The amount of S is found by using the expression

$$n = \frac{m}{M}$$

where m = 16.0 g and M = 32.1 g mol^{-1}

$$\therefore n = \frac{m}{M} = \frac{16.0 \text{ g}}{32.1 \text{ g mol}^{-1}} = 0.498 \text{ mol}$$

$\therefore$ the amount of Mg also = 0.498 mol

The mass of Mg is found by using the expression

$n = \frac{m}{M}$ in the form $m = nM$

where n = 0.498 mol and M = 24.3 g mol^{-1}

$\therefore m = nM$ = 0.498 mol × 24.3 g mol^{-1} = $\boxed{12.1 \text{ g}}$

(b) For NaNO$_3$, $n = \frac{m}{M} = \frac{4.25 \text{ g}}{85.0 \text{ g mol}^{-1}} = 0.0500 \text{ mol}$

But amount of O$_2$ = ½ × amount of NaNO$_3$

= ½ × 0.0500 mol = 0.0250 mol

For O$_2$, $m = nM$ = 0.0250 mol × 32.0 g mol^{-1} = $\boxed{0.800 \text{ g}}$

Exercise 19

For P, substituting into the expression

$$n = \frac{m}{M}$$

where m = 4.00 g and M = 31.0 g mol^{-1}

gives $n = \frac{m}{M} = \frac{4.00 \text{ g}}{31.0 \text{ g mol}^{-1}} = 0.129 \text{ mol}$

From the equation,

$$\frac{\text{amount of P}_2\text{O}_5}{\text{amount of P}} = \frac{2}{4} = \frac{1}{2}$$

$\therefore$ amount of P$_2$O$_5$ = ½ × amount of P

= ½ × 0.129 mol = 0.0645 mol

For P$_2$O$_5$, substituting into the expression

$n = \frac{m}{M}$ in the form $m = nM$

where n = 0.0645 mol and M = 142 g mol^{-1}

gives m = 0.0645 mol × 142 g mol^{-1} = $\boxed{9.16 \text{ g}}$

Exercise 20

The reacting amount of Al is given by substituting into the expression

$$n = \frac{m}{M}$$

where m = 0.27 g and M = 27.0 g mol^{-1}

$$\therefore n = \frac{0.27 \text{ g}}{27.0 \text{ g mol}^{-1}} = 0.010 \text{ mol}$$

The amount of Cu formed is given by substituting into the expression

$$n = \frac{m}{M}$$

where m = 0.96 g and M = 63.8 g mol^{-1}

$$\therefore n = \frac{0.96 \text{ g}}{63.5 \text{ g mol}^{-1}} = 0.015 \text{ mol}$$

$$\therefore \frac{\text{amount of Al}}{\text{amount of Cu}} = \frac{0.010 \text{ mol}}{0.015 \text{ mol}} = \frac{2}{3}$$

We can build up the equation from this ratio

2Al(s) + ? CuSO$_4$(aq) → 3Cu(s) + ? Al$_2$(SO$_4$)$_3$(aq)

To equalise Cu atoms, the stoichiometric coefficient for CuSO$_4$ must be 3.
To equalise Al atoms, the stoichiometric coefficient for Al$_2$(SO$_4$)$_3$ must be 1.

$\therefore$ $\boxed{\text{2Al(s) + 3CuSO}_4\text{(aq)} \rightarrow \text{3Cu(s) + Al}_2\text{(SO}_4\text{)}_3\text{(aq)}}$

Exercise 23

	$BaCl_2$	H_2O
Mass/g	8.53	1.47
Molar mass/g mol^{-1}	208.2	18.0
Amount/mol	$\dfrac{8.53}{208.2} = 0.0410$	$\dfrac{1.47}{18.0} = 0.0817$
Amount/smallest amount = relative amount	$\dfrac{0.0410}{0.0410} = 1.00$	$\dfrac{0.0817}{0.0410} = 1.99$
Simplest ratio	1	2

The formula is $BaCl_2 \cdot 2H_2O$, i.e. $\boxed{x = 2}$

Exercise 24

The mass of water removed = 0.585 g - 0.535 g = 0.050 g

	$UO(C_2O_4) \cdot 6H_2O$	H_2O (removed)
Mass/g	0.585	0.050
Molar mass/g mol^{-1}	450	18.0
Amount/mol	$\dfrac{0.585}{450} = 0.00130$	$\dfrac{0.050}{18.0} = 0.0028$
Amount/smallest amount = relative amount	$\dfrac{0.00130}{0.00130} = 1.00$	$\dfrac{0.0028}{0.0013} = 2.2$
Simplest ratio	1	2

Thus, the ratio of the amount of original compound to the removed water is 1:2. This means that for every 1 mol of compound, 2 mol of water were removed. The resulting substance would therefore have the formula $UO(C_2O_4) \cdot 4H_2O$.

Exercise 25

	C	H	O
Mass/g	40.0 g	6.6 g	53.4 g
Molar mass/g mol^{-1}	12.0	1.0	16.0
Amount/mol	$\dfrac{40.0}{12.0} = 3.33$	$\dfrac{6.6}{1.0} = 6.6$	$\dfrac{53.4}{16.0} = 3.34$
Amount/smallest amount = relative amount	$\dfrac{3.33}{3.33} = 1.00$	$\dfrac{6.6}{3.33} = 1.98$	$\dfrac{3.34}{3.33} = 1.00$
Simplest ratio	1	2	1

The empirical formula is $\boxed{CH_2O}$

Exercise 21

We must calculate the amount of each reagent to determine which limits the reaction.

For Fe, substituting into the expression

$$n = \frac{m}{M}$$

where m = 2.8 g and M = 55.8 g mol^{-1}

gives $n = \dfrac{2.8 \text{ g}}{55.8 \text{ g mol}^{-1}} = 0.050$ mol

For S, substituting into the expression

$$n = \frac{m}{M}$$

where m = 2.0 g and M = 32.1 g mol^{-1}

gives $n = \dfrac{2.0 \text{ g}}{32.1 \text{ g mol}^{-1}} = 0.062$ mol

From the equation, one mole of iron reacts with one mole of sulphur, so the amount of iron limits the amount of iron(II) sulphide formed.

∴ amount of FeS = amount of Fe = 0.050 mol

Substituting into the expression

$$n = \frac{m}{M} \text{ in the form } m = nM$$

where n = 0.050 mol and M = 87.9 g mol^{-1}

gives $m = 0.050 \text{ mol} \times 87.9 \text{ g mol}^{-1} = \boxed{4.4 \text{ g}}$

Exercise 22

	Co	S	O	H_2O
Mass/g	2.10	1.14	2.28	4.50
Molar mass/ g mol^{-1}	58.9	32.1	16.0	18.0
Amount/mol	$\dfrac{2.10}{58.9} = 0.0357$	$\dfrac{1.14}{32.1} = 0.0355$	$\dfrac{2.28}{16.0} = 0.143$	$\dfrac{4.50}{18.0} = 0.250$
Amount/ smallest amount = relative amount	$\dfrac{0.0357}{0.0355} = 1.01$	$\dfrac{0.0355}{0.0355} = 1.00$	$\dfrac{0.143}{0.0355} = 4.03$	$\dfrac{0.250}{0.0355} = 7.04$
Simplest ratio	1	1	4	7

The formula is $\boxed{CoSO_4 \cdot 7H_2O}$

Exercise 28

(a) Substituting into the expression

$$c = \frac{n}{V}$$

where n = 0.100 mol and V = (2000/1000) dm³ = $\boxed{0.0500 \text{ mol dm}^{-3}}$

gives $c = \dfrac{0.100 \text{ mol}}{2.00 \text{ dm}^3} = \boxed{0.100 \text{ mol dm}^{-3}}$

(b) $c = \dfrac{n}{V} = \dfrac{0.0100 \text{ mol}}{1.00 \text{ dm}^3} = \boxed{0.100 \text{ mol dm}^{-3}}$

(c) $c = \dfrac{n}{V} = \dfrac{0.100 \text{ mol}}{0.500 \text{ dm}^3} = \boxed{0.200 \text{ mol dm}^{-3}}$

(d) $c = \dfrac{n}{V} = \dfrac{0.100 \text{ mol}}{0.250 \text{ dm}^3} = \boxed{0.400 \text{ mol dm}^{-3}}$

(e) $c = \dfrac{n}{V} = \dfrac{0.100 \text{ mol}}{0.100 \text{ dm}^3} = \boxed{1.00 \text{ mol dm}^{-3}}$

Exercise 29

(a) Substituting into the expression

$$n = \frac{m}{M}$$

where m = 8.50 g and M = 169.9 g mol⁻¹

gives $n = \dfrac{8.50 \text{ g}}{169.9 \text{ g mol}^{-1}} = 0.0500 \text{ mol}$

Substituting into the expression

$$c = \frac{n}{V}$$

where n = 0.0500 mol and V = 1.00 dm³

gives $c = \dfrac{0.0500 \text{ mol}}{1.00 \text{ dm}^3} = 0.0500 \text{ mol dm}^{-3}$

Or, substituting $n = \dfrac{m}{M}$ into $c = \dfrac{n}{V}$

$c = \dfrac{m}{MV} = \dfrac{8.50 \text{ g}}{169.9 \text{ g mol}^{-1} \times 1.00 \text{ dm}^3} = \boxed{0.0500 \text{ mol dm}^{-3}}$

(b) $c = \dfrac{m}{MV} = \dfrac{10.7 \text{ g}}{214.0 \text{ g mol}^{-1} \times 0.250 \text{ dm}^3} = \boxed{0.200 \text{ mol dm}^{-3}}$

(c) $c = \dfrac{m}{MV} = \dfrac{11.2 \text{ g}}{331.2 \text{ g mol}^{-1} \times 0.050 \text{ dm}^3} = \boxed{0.676 \text{ mol dm}^{-3}}$

(d) $c = \dfrac{m}{MV} = \dfrac{14.3 \text{ g}}{294.1 \text{ g mol}^{-1} \times 0.250 \text{ dm}^3} = \boxed{0.194 \text{ mol dm}^{-3}}$

(e) $c = \dfrac{m}{MV} = \dfrac{11.9 \text{ g}}{249.6 \text{ g mol}^{-1} \times 0.500 \text{ dm}^3} = \boxed{0.0954 \text{ mol dm}^{-3}}$

Exercise 26

	Na	Al	Si	O	H_2O
Mass/g	12.1	14.2	22.1	42.1	9.48
Molar mass/g mol⁻¹	23.0	27.0	28.1	16.0	18.0
Amount/mol	$\frac{12.1}{23.0}$ = 0.526	$\frac{14.2}{27.0}$ = 0.526	$\frac{22.1}{28.1}$ = 0.786	$\frac{42.1}{16.0}$ = 2.63	$\frac{9.48}{18.0}$ = 0.527
Amount/smallest amount = relative amount	$\frac{0.526}{0.526}$ = 1.00	$\frac{0.526}{0.526}$ = 1.00	$\frac{0.786}{0.526}$ = 1.49	$\frac{2.63}{0.526}$ = 5.00	$\frac{0.527}{0.526}$ = 1.00
Simplest ratio	2	2	3	10	2

Note: Since 1.49 is very close to 1.5, we are justified in rounding up. The empirical formula is $\boxed{Na_2Al_2Si_3O_{10}\cdot 2H_2O}$.

Exercise 27

	C	H	O
Mass/g	3.91	0.87	5.22
Molar mass/g mol⁻¹	12.0	1.0	16.0
Amount/mol	0.326	0.87	0.326
Amount/smallest amount = relative amount	$\frac{0.326}{0.326}$ = 1.00	$\frac{0.87}{0.326}$ = 2.67	$\frac{0.326}{0.326}$ = 1.00
Simplest ratio	3	8	3

Note: We are not justified in rounding off 2.67 to 3. 2.67 is the decimal equivalent of 8/3, so we treble the relative amounts, thus converting 2.67 to 8. The resulting empirical formula is $\boxed{C_3H_8O_3}$.

Experiment 2 - Specimen Results

Results Table 6

Molar mass of potassium hydrogenphthalate, M	204.1 g mol^{-1}
Mass of bottle and contents before transfer, m_1	15.47 g
Mass of bottle and contents after transfer, m_2	10.20 g
Mass of potassium hydrogenphthalate, $m = (m_1 - m_2)$	5.27 g
Amount of potassium hydrogenphthalate, $n = m/M$	2.58×10^{-2} mol
Volume of solution, V	0.250 dm^3
Concentration of potassium hydrogenphthalate, $c = n/V$	0.103 mol dm^{-3}

Experiment 2 - Questions

1. (a) The concentration would be lower than calculated. From the expression $c = n/V$, a decrease in amount will reduce the value of the concentration.

   (b) The concentration would be greater than calculated. From the expression $c = n/V$, insufficient water (i.e. a decrease in V) will increase the value of the concentration.

Exercise 30

(a) Substituting into the expression

$c = \dfrac{n}{V}$ in the form $n = cV$

where c = 5.00 mol dm^{-3} and V = 4.00 dm^3

gives n = 5.00 mol dm^{-3} × 4.00 dm^3 × 1.00 dm^3 = $\boxed{20.0 \text{ mol}}$

(b) $n = cV$ = 2.50 mol dm^{-3} × 1.00 dm^3 = $\boxed{2.50 \text{ mol}}$

(c) $n = cV$ = 0.439 mol dm^{-3} × 0.020 dm^3 = $\boxed{8.78 \times 10^{-3} \text{ mol}}$

Exercise 31

(a) Substituting into the expression

$c = \dfrac{n}{V}$ in the form $n = cV$

where c = 0.100 mol dm^{-3} and V = 1.00 dm^3

gives n = 0.100 mol dm^{-3} × 1.00 dm^3 = 0.100 mol

Substituting into the expression

$n = \dfrac{m}{M}$ in the form $m = nM$

where n = 0.100 mol and M = 58.4 g mol^{-1}

gives m = 0.100 mol × 58.4 g mol^{-1} = 5.84 g

Or, combining $c = \dfrac{n}{V}$ with $n = \dfrac{m}{M}$ and substituting

$m = nM = cVM$ = 0.100 mol dm^{-3} × 1.00 dm^3 × 58.4 g mol^{-1} = $\boxed{5.84 \text{ g}}$

(b) $m = cVM$ = 1.00 mol dm^{-3} × 0.500 dm^3 × 110.9 g mol^{-1} = $\boxed{55.5 \text{ g}}$

(c) $m = cVM$ = 0.200 mol dm^{-3} × 0.250 dm^3 × 158.0 g mol^{-1} = $\boxed{7.90 \text{ g}}$

(d) $m = cVM$ = 0.117 mol dm^{-3} × 0.200 dm^3 × 40.0 g mol^{-1} = $\boxed{0.936 \text{ g}}$

Exercise 32

(a) $Ba(OH)_2(aq) + 2HCl(aq) \rightarrow BaCl_2(aq) + 2H_2O(l)$

Let A refer to HCl and B to Ba(OH)$_2$

Substituting into the expression

$\dfrac{c_A V_A}{c_B V_B} = \dfrac{a}{b}$

where c_A = 0.0600 mol dm^{-3} c_B = ?

V_A = 25.0 cm^3 V_B = 20.0 cm^3

a = 2 b = 1

gives $\dfrac{0.600 \text{ mol dm}^{-3} \times 25.0 \text{ cm}^3}{c_B \times 20.0 \text{ cm}^3} = \dfrac{2}{1}$

Solving for c_B gives

$c_B = \dfrac{0.0600 \text{ mol dm}^{-3} \times 25.0 \text{ cm}^3}{2 \times 20.0 \text{ cm}^3}$ = $\boxed{0.0375 \text{ mol dm}^{-3}}$

(b) It is not necessary to convert from cm^3 to dm^3 because the units of volume cancel in the final expression.

Results Table 7

Pipette solution	potassium hydrogenphthalate				0.0103 mol dm⁻³	25.0 cm³
Burette solution	sodium hydroxide				? mol dm⁻³	
Indicator	phenolphthalein					

		Trial	1	2	3	(4)
Burette readings	Final	26.9	26.80	27.45	26.15	-
	Initial	0.7	0.90	1.50	0.30	-
Volume used (titre)/cm³		26.2	25.90	25.95	25.85	-
Mean titre/cm³		25.9(0)				

Calculation

Let A refer to potassium hydrogenphthalate and B to sodium hydroxide.

1. Substituting into the expression

$$\frac{c_A V_A}{c_B V_B} = \frac{a}{b}$$

where c_A = 0.103 mol dm⁻³ c_B = ?

V_A = 25.0 cm³ V_B = 25.9 cm³

a = 1 b = 1

gives $\dfrac{0.103 \text{ mol dm}^{-3} \times 25.0 \text{ cm}^3}{c_B \times 25.9 \text{ cm}^3} = \dfrac{1}{1}$

∴ $c_B = \dfrac{0.103 \text{ mol dm}^{-3} \times 25.0 \text{ cm}^3}{25.9 \text{ cm}^3}$ = $\boxed{0.0994 \text{ mol dm}^{-3}}$

Experiment 3 - Questions

1. (a) If the burette is dry, no effect. If the burette is wet, this will slightly dilute the NaOH so that the calculated concentration will be less than the actual concentration.

   (b) If the pipette is dry, no effect. If the pipette is wet, this will slightly dilute the measured volume of HA so that less NaOH will be required to neutralise it. The calculated concentration of NaOH will be lower than the actual concentration.

   (c) The calculated concentration of NaOH will be lower than the actual concentration.

   (d) No effect. The dilution occurs after the amount has been measured.

2. It is easier for the eye to detect the approach of the end-point when colour appears rather than when it disappears.

3. Sodium hydroxide solution attacks glass to some extent, especially the ground surfaces in some burette taps. Also, it absorbs carbon dioxide from the air forming a crust of sodium carbonate. Both these actions can cause burette taps to seize up.

Exercise 33

(a) NaOH(aq) + HNO₃(aq) → NaNO₃(aq) + H₂O(l)

Let A refer to NaOH and B to HNO₃

Substituting into the expression

$$\frac{c_A V_A}{c_B V_B} = \frac{a}{b}$$

where c_A = 0.500 mol dm⁻³ c_B = 0.100 mol dm⁻³

V_A = ? V_B = 50.0 cm³

$\dfrac{a}{b} = \dfrac{1}{1}$

gives $V_A = \dfrac{0.100 \text{ mol dm}^{-3} \times 50.0 \text{ cm}^3}{0.500 \text{ mol dm}^{-3}}$

∴ $V_A = \dfrac{0.100 \text{ mol dm}^{-3} \times 50.0 \text{ cm}^3}{0.500 \text{ mol dm}^{-3}}$ = $\boxed{10.0 \text{ cm}^3}$

(b) $\dfrac{c_A V_A}{c_B V_B} = \dfrac{a}{b}$ (A refers to NaOH, B to H₂SO₄).

∴ $\dfrac{0.500 \text{ mol dm}^{-3} \times V_A}{0.262 \text{ mol dm}^{-3} \times 22.5 \text{ cm}^3} = \dfrac{2}{1}$

and $V_A = \dfrac{2 \times 0.262 \times 22.5 \text{ cm}^3}{0.500}$ = $\boxed{23.6 \text{ cm}^3}$

Exercise 34

Substituting into the expression:

$$\frac{c_A V_A}{c_B V_B} = \frac{a}{b}$$

where c_A = 0.50 mol dm⁻³ c_B = 0.20 mol dm⁻³

V_A = 25.0 cm³ V_B = 31.3 cm³

$\dfrac{a}{b} = \dfrac{0.50 \text{ mol dm}^{-3} \times 25.0 \text{ cm}^3}{0.20 \text{ mol dm}^{-3} \times 31.3 \text{ cm}^3} = \dfrac{2}{1}$

∴ $\boxed{a = 2, \; b = 1}$

Results Table 9

Mass of bottle and contents before transfer, m_1	11.79 g	
Mass of bottle and contents after transfer, m_2	10.21 g	
Mass of sample, $m = (m_1 - m_2)$	1.58 g	
Mass of $BaCl_2 \cdot 2H_2O$ in 10.0 cm³	0.0632 g	

Results Table 10

Pipette solution	barium chloride	?	mol dm⁻³	10.0 cm³
Burette solution	silver nitrate	0.0506	mol dm⁻³	
Indicator	potassium chromate(VI)			

		Trial	1	2	3	(4)
Burette readings	Final	10.4	20.65	30.40	41.10	-
	Initial	0.0	10.40	20.75	30.90	-
Volume used (titre)/cm³		10.4	10.25	10.15	10.20	-
Mean titre/cm³		10.2(0)				

Exercise 35   See overleaf.

Exercise 36

(a) 3   (b) 4   (c) 2   (d) 3   (e) 3   (f) 5   (g) 4   (h) 3 or 4

(i) 3, 4, 5 or 6

Exercise 37

(a) 208 g   (b) 0.649 dm³

Exercise 38

(a) 3.4 m   (b) 76 cm³

Exercise 39

(a) 3.0 x 10⁻³ mol   (b) 67.8 g

Exercise 40

(a) 0.48 mol   (b) 2 g cm⁻³

Experiment 4 - Specimen Results

Results Table 8

Pipette solution	iodine	0.0497	mol dm⁻³	10.0 cm³
Burette solution	sodium thiosulphate	0.0512	mol dm⁻³	
Indicator	starch			

		Trial	1	2	3	(4)
Burette readings	Final	20.3	40.40	20.15	40.25	-
	Initial	0.0	20.30	0.10	20.15	-
Volume used (titre)/cm³		20.3	20.10	20.05	20.10	-
Mean titre/cm³		20.1(0)				

Calculation

1. Substituting into the expression

$$\frac{c_A V_A}{c_B V_B} = \frac{a}{b}$$ (A refers to $Na_2S_2O_3$, B to I_2)

where c_A = 0.0512 mol dm⁻³ c_B = 0.0497 mol dm⁻³

V_A = 20.1 cm³ V_B = 10.0 cm³

a = ? b = ?

gives $\dfrac{a}{b} = \dfrac{0.0512 \text{ mol dm}^{-3} \times 20.1 \text{ cm}^3}{0.0497 \text{ mol dm}^{-3} \times 10.0 \text{ cm}^3} = \dfrac{2.07}{1}$

∴ a = 2 and b = 1

So we can write for the equation:

$2Na_2S_2O_3(aq) + I_2(aq) \rightarrow$ Products

2. The formula for the other compound is $Na_2S_4O_6$ (sodium tetrathionate).

$2Na_2S_2O_3(aq) + I_2(aq) \rightarrow NaI(aq) +$?

To balance I atoms, the stoichiometric coefficient of NaI must be 2.

$2Na_2S_2O_3(aq) + I_2(aq) \rightarrow 2NaI +$?

The atoms unaccounted for are two of sodium, four of sulphur and six of oxygen, $Na_2S_4O_6$.

The balanced equation is

$\boxed{2Na_2S_2O_3(aq) + I_2(aq) \rightarrow 2NaI(aq) + Na_2S_4O_6(aq)}$

(The empirical formula is NaS_2O_3, but $Na_2S_4O_6$ is preferred because it contains $S_4O_6^{2-}$ ions.)

Exercise 35

First calculate the mass of Mg^{2+}, Cl^- and H_2O in the 0.203 g sample. The mass of Cl^- can be calculated from the titration data, the mass of H_2O from the % lost on dehydration and finally the mass of Mg^{2+} by difference.

Next, convert masses to relative amounts to give values for m and n.

The procedure can be summarised in a flow-chart, as follows:

EQUATION → relative amounts

VOL. AgNO₃ → amount Ag → amount Cl → mass Cl
CONCN. AgNO₃

MASS SALT → mass Mg → amount Mg → FORMULA

% LOSS → mass H₂O → amount H₂O

The detailed calculation follows, step by step:

1. Amount and mass of Cl
$$Ag^+(aq) + Cl^-(aq) \rightarrow AgCl(s)$$
∴ amount of Cl = amount of AgNO₃
$$= cV = 0.100 \text{ mol dm}^{-3} \times 0.0200 \text{ dm}^3 = 2.00 \times 10^{-3} \text{ mol}$$
∴ mass of Cl $= nM = 2.00 \times 10^{-3} \text{ mol} \times 35.5 \text{ g mol}^{-1} = 0.0710 \text{ g}$

2. Mass and amount of H₂O
mass of H₂O = loss in mass of sample
$$= \frac{53.2}{100} \times 0.203 \text{ g} = 0.108 \text{ g}$$
∴ amount of H₂O $= \dfrac{m}{M} = \dfrac{0.108 \text{ g}}{18.0 \text{ g mol}^{-1}} = 6.00 \times 10^{-3} \text{ mol}$

3. Mass and amount of Mg
mass of Mg = mass of salt - mass of Cl - mass of H₂O
$$= 0.203 - 0.071 \text{ g} - 0.108 \text{ g} = 0.024 \text{ g}$$
∴ amount of Mg $= \dfrac{m}{M} = \dfrac{0.024 \text{ g}}{24 \text{ g mol}^{-1}} = 1.0 \times 10^{-3} \text{ mol}$

4. Relative amounts

	Mg	Cl	H₂O
Amount/mol	1.0×10^{-3}	2.0×10^{-3}	6.0×10^{-3}
Amount/smallest amount	$\frac{1.0}{1.0}$	$\frac{2.0}{1.0}$	$\frac{6.0}{1.0}$
= relative amount	= 1.0	= 2.0	= 6.0

∴ $m = 2$, $n = 6$ and the formula is $\boxed{MgCl_2 \cdot 6H_2O}$

Experiment 5 - Calculation

There is more than one way of tackling this problem. Here is one suggestion.
First calculate the masses of $BaCl_2$ and H_2O in each sample. The mass of $BaCl_2$ can be calculated indirectly from titration data and the mass of H_2O by difference.

Next convert masses to relative amounts to determine x. We explain this step by step.

1. Amount of Cl in sample (as Cl⁻)
$$Ag^+(aq) + Cl^-(aq) \rightarrow AgCl(s)$$
∴ amount of Cl = amount of AgNO₃
$$= cV = 0.0506 \text{ mol dm}^{-3} \times 0.0102 \text{ dm}^3 = 5.16 \times 10^{-4} \text{ mol}$$

2. Amount and mass of BaCl₂
$$BaCl_2(s) + aq \rightarrow Ba^{2+}(aq) + 2Cl^-(aq)$$
∴ amount of BaCl₂ $= \frac{1}{2} \times$ amount of Cl⁻
$$= \frac{1}{2} \times 5.16 \times 10^{-4} \text{ mol} = 2.58 \times 10^{-4} \text{ mol}$$
mass of BaCl₂ $= nM = 2.58 \times 10^{-4} \text{ mol} \times 208 \text{ g mol}^{-1} = 0.0537 \text{ g}$

3. Mass and amount of H₂O
mass of H₂O = mass of BaCl₂·xH₂O - mass of BaCl₂
$$= 0.0632 \text{ g} - 0.0537 \text{ g} = 0.0095 \text{ g}$$
amount of H₂O $= \dfrac{m}{M} = \dfrac{0.0095 \text{ g}}{18.0 \text{ g mol}^{-1}} = 5.3 \times 10^{-4} \text{ mol}$

4. Relative amounts

	BaCl₂	H₂O
Amount/mol	2.58×10^{-4}	5.3×10^{-4}
Amount/smallest amount	$\frac{2.58 \times 10^{-4}}{2.58 \times 10^{-4}}$	$\frac{5.3 \times 10^{-4}}{2.58 \times 10^{-4}}$
= relative amount	= 1.00	= 2.1

The relative amounts are very close to the integers 1 and 2.
∴ $x = 2$ and the formula is $\boxed{BaCl_2 \cdot 2H_2O}$